NAVIGATOR

MEN'S DEVELOPMENT WORKBOOK

developed and written by

James Traeger, Jenny Daisley and Liz Willis

HAWTHORN PRESS

Navigator © 1999, 2006 James Traeger, Jenny Daisley and Liz Willis

James Traeger, Jenny Daisley and Liz Willis are hereby identified as authors of this work in accordance with Section 77 of the Copyright, Designs and Patent Act, 1988. They assert and give notice of their moral right under this Act.

Published by Hawthorn Press
Hawthorn House, 1 Lansdown Lane, Stroud, Gloucestershire, GL5 1BJ, UK.
Tel 01453 757040 Fax 01453 751138
E-mail info@hawthornpress.com Website **www.hawthornpress.com**

Acknowledgements

Human Family by Maya Angelou reprinted by kind permission of Time Warner Book Group. He was a Man from *Poems: 1972-2002* by Michael Leunig reprinted by kind permission of Penguin Books Australia Ltd. Excerpted from *I Will Not Die an Unlived Life* by Dawna Markova, with permission from Conari Press, imprint of Red Wheel/Wieser. From *Letters to a Young Poet* by Rainer Maria Rilke, translated by M D Herter Norton, copyright 1934, 1954, by W W Norton & Company Inc, renewed © 1962, 1982, by M D Herter Norton. Used by permission of W W Norton & Company Inc. Rumi from *Selected poems from the Divani Shamsi Tabriz,* edited and translated with an Introduction, Notes and Appendices by Reynold A Nicolson, 1989, reprinted by kind permission of Cambridge University Press. Tao te Ching by Lao Tzu, a new English version with foreword and notes by Stephen Mitchell. All other poems in this book are in the public domain.

The 7 Habits of Highly Effective People, Copyright © Stephen Covey, 2004 first published in Great Britain by Pocket Books, an imprint of Simon & Schuster UK Ltd. *Multiple intelligences: the theory in practice,* Howard Gardner, published by Perseus Books Group, USA, 1993. *Knights Without Armor: A Guide to the Inner Lives of Men,* Dr Aaron Kipnis, published by Indigo Phoenix Books, USA, 2004. *How to Build a Life-Changing Men's Ministry: Bringing the Fire Home to your Church,* Steve Sonderman, Bethany House Publishers, Minneapolis, a division of Baker Publishing Group, USA, 1996.

Every effort has been made to trace the ownership of all copyrighted material. If any omission has been made, please bring this to the publisher's attention so that proper acknowledgement may be given in future editions.

Cover design by Patrick Roe, Southgate Solutions Ltd
Designed and typeset by Hawthorn Press Ltd, Stroud
Illustrations by Frances Fineran

First edition 1999
Reprinted 2001, 2002, 2004, 2005
Second edition 2006
Printed by The Bath Press, Bath

Printed on Evolve Offset. 100% recycled and totally chlorine-free.

Previous works by Liz Willis and Jenny Daisley
Springboard Women's Development Workbook 2000 Hawthorn Press
Developing Women through Training 1997 The Springboard Consultancy
The Assertive Trainer 1994 McGraw Hill
Women Singled Out 1995 The Springboard Consultancy

ISBN 1 903 458 61 7
978-1-903458-61-7

Contents

Objective: To get you started on the Navigator programme.
- Getting started • Why development and why personal?
- How Navigator works • Choosing your route

Objective: Looking at the wider issues around development
and change.
- Life as a journey • The luck challenge • Working with change
- A man's world • Taking responsibility for yourself

Objective: To clarify what is important in your life, how you see
yourself and how this compares with how others see you.
- Your values • Your identity • Celebrating diversity and
overcoming prejudice • Your attitudes • Superman or supermen?

Objective: To review your journey so far, consider where you
are now and explore possible options for your next steps.
- Where have you been, and which way now? • Your Life Map
- Where are you going? • Your goal strategy

Objective: To develop a goal strategy that provides steps for
action which are SMART: specific, measurable, achievable,
realistic and time-bound.
- World goals • Your goal strategy • Picture your goals
- Your strategy document

Objective: To explore the way you think and the tools you can use to become more effective.

• What you think and how you think • Positive thinking
• Intuition – the sixth sense • Your creativity

Objectives: To be clear about the messages you want to give about yourself. To look at the most effective ways of putting that message across.

• Getting yourself across • Why manage your image?
• Your visibility • The image/message link • Assertiveness
• Assertiveness in practice • Meaningful mission statement

• A space and encouragement to write your own story
• Your Notes

• The Authors • Useful organisations • Websites

• Books • Films • Inspirational songs • Inspirational poems

Getting in Touch

This workbook is part of the Navigator Men's Development programme which has been researched and developed as a programme for men parallel to the award-winning Springboard Women's Development programme.

This book is designed to be used as part of the Navigator programme, which will give you the support of other people and short workshops to help you get the best out of this book. Get in touch with us and we'll send you the list of licensed Navigator trainers who can tell you what is happening in your area.

There is also an international Springboard Consultancy Newsletter – 'NewsSplash' – which provides information and networking links for anyone interested or involved in Springboard or Navigator, whether you are an individual, an employer or representing an organisation. Contact us for details of 'NewsSplash'.

Many Navigator and Springboard programmes are run inside organisations. Only trainers trained by us are licensed to run Navigator or Springboard programmes. Contact us for further details about how to implement a Navigator or Springboard programme in-house, or about how to become a licensed trainer.

We look forward to hearing from you. To get in touch, send this form or write to:
The Springboard Consultancy Ltd, Holwell, East Down, Barnstaple, Devon, EX31 4NZ, UK.
Tel 01271 850828 Fax 01271 850130. E-mail office@springboardconsultancy.com
Website www.springboardconsultancy.com

Tick the box(es) which apply to you: * delete as appropriate

❑ I am interested in attending a *Navigator or Springboard programme. Please send me the list of local licensed trainers.

❑ I would like information on becoming a freelance *Navigator or Springboard licensed trainer

❑ I would like information on licensing in-house *Navigator or Springboard trainers

❑ I would like further information about how to implement *Navigator and/or Springboard programmes within my organisation

❑ I would like to be put on the 'NewsSplash' mailing list

❑ I would like information on programmes for managers and programmes on creativity.

Name _____ Date _____

Job Title (if applicable) _____

Organisation (if applicable) _____

Address _____

_____

_____ Postcode _____

Daytime Tel. No. _____ Evening Tel. No. _____

Biographical details of the authors

James Traeger is a pioneer of men's development in the UK and beyond. He has over 15 years unique experience of leading the research, development and delivery of learning events specifically addressing the lives and choices of men in the workplace and beyond.

He has piloted and run Navigator programmes that have benefited thousands of men, as well as trained over 30 other men to run the Navigator programme, internationally, since 1999, in association with the award-winning Springboard Consultancy. As well as for men's development and Navigator, he is highly respected as a leadership development consultant and coach, and has an impressive client list right across the spectrum of private and public sectors.

He also has a strong academic as well as commercial strand running through his career. As well as being a visiting lecturer at Surrey University, he is currently researching his doctorate as part of the highly prestigious Centre for Action Research in Professional Practice at the University of Bath. In business, he was a production manager in the theatre (winning a 'fringe first' at the 1988 Edinburgh Festival) and then general manager of a leading commercial photo agency before going fully self-employed in the mid-1990s.

He also values community involvement, and is a school governor and local organiser in his hometown of East Molesey, Surrey, and a devoted and involved father to Max and Jessica.

James is well respected as a skilled facilitator and conference speaker and is acclaimed for his pioneering work in the field of personal and organisational development and gender awareness.

Biographical details of the authors

Jenny Daisley and Liz Willis are well known as two of the UK's leading women's development consultants, with a combined experience of over 55 years in this field. In addition to their consultancy and training work, they are also known as writers on training and personal development issues and have four published books.

Jenny and Liz are especially known as innovators and designers of new forms of training and their work with James Traeger in developing this Navigator workbook is no exception. They have a positive and practical approach and work at all levels in organisations, creating overall development strategies as well as designing and developing a variety of training, from in-depth residential courses for small groups, to one-day events with hundreds.

Together, they run The Springboard Consultancy where they work nationally and internationally with clients in the public, private, voluntary and academic sectors. They are probably best known for their creation of the award-winning Springboard Women's Development Programme, which has reached over 160,000 women in twenty different countries. This was made possible by the setting up of an extensive international network of over 700 Springboard trainers, all especially selected and trained by Jenny and/or Liz.

Whilst Jenny and Liz have a high profile in the Women's Development world, both of them have also worked in main-stream training and development. They also have personal experience of having started at the bottom of organisations and working their way up to management positions, experiencing the satisfactions and frustrations of everyday employment along the way. They have also developed the Spring Forward programme for men and women on their way up and The Purple Process – a programme on creativity and innovation.

Thanks Writing this book has involved many men and women co-operating to bring about Jenny Daisley's pioneering vision of a new opportunity for men to work together on their personal and professional development, in parallel with her innovative years of work with women. The vital step forward in turning this vision into reality was meeting and working with James Traeger, who had a similar vision for men and his own track record in men's development. This book is the result of two years of collaboration, research and development, involving a wide range of people (whether it was supporting the initial vision or checking the final manuscript). We would like to thank them all.

In particular:

– the pioneering organisations who formed the **Research Consortium**, who, over two years, gave us access to men and their managers to identify their developmental needs, collect information and statistics and in many cases run and evaluate pilot programmes. They are: **BT Mobile, Braintree District Council, Direct Services, Wolverhampton MBC, Midland Bank PLC, NatWest UK, The Stationery Office, The University of Cambridge** and **The University of London**.

– **Hampshire County Council, Knowsley Metropolitan Borough Council, MCL Group** and the **Oxford Radcliffe Hospitals NHS Trust** for hosting further pilot programmes.

– **the men on pilot Navigator programmes**, on experience weekends and in research groups for their input on early drafts, and for providing their stories. The feedback and ideas from these pilot programmes and research have substantially contributed to the final result.

– **John Lewis** and **Norman Neal** of Wolverhampton MBC, **Peter Bystricky** of Cambridge University and **Andy Durkin** and **Mark Bunyan** for bravely offering their own personal examples.

– The thousands of men who have been through the programme since 1999, in the UK, Ireland, Australia and Finland
– The Brookfield Men's Development Group
– John Ruskin, PR Consultant
– Adrian Price and Hampshire County Council
– Sue Pandey and Cambridge University Staff Development Unit
– Hugh Dennis, Adrian Price, Jon Toulson and Chris Sharpe of the materials updating group.

– **Patrick Roe** for the cover design.
– **Chris Sharpe, Johan Henri Quanjer, David Bancroft Turner** and **Don Morley** for their valuable comments on the manuscript.

ix

THANKS

– the **UK licensed Springboard trainers** who have given encouragement and feedback.

– **Nicola Smith, Liza Edwards** and **Celia Morrison-Smith** in the Springboard office for their good humour, patience and sheer hard work in making this happen initially and **Georgina Pullen** for keeping it going.

– **Frances Fineran** of Hawthorn Press for her professionalism, good humour and creativity in interpreting our wishes through our many successive drafts.

In addition, Jenny and Liz especially want to thank:

– **James Traeger** for bringing his passion for men's development and for his openness and courage. We also respect his commitment to the project, his interpretation of all the feedback and creativity in developing new material. The creation of the Navigator programme as the brother programme to our award-winning Springboard Women's Development programme means that thousands of men have the opportunity to reap similar benefits to those experienced by women using the Springboard programme.

– the international network of pioneering Navigator trainers.

Finally, James would particularly like to thank:

– **Jenny Daisley** and **Liz Willis**, who, having excelled in the field of developing women, had the vision to recognise that everyone stands to benefit from men also being clear about themselves, their aims and their behaviour. Without Jenny, Liz and all the women from Springboard, there would be no Navigator programme.

– Inspirational friends and mentors, greatly missed: **John Henri Quanjer**, 1934-2001, **Robert O'Neil Crossman**, 1947-1996.

– my wife **Gillie**, and children **Max** and **Jessica** for all their love and support.

James Traeger, Jenny Daisley & Liz Willis
2005

Foreword

I first encountered Navigator in the late 1990s when I was asked by a senior manager at LSE if there was a parallel programme for men to run alongside the Springboard programme we were just introducing for female staff.

This request to venture into the uncharted world of development for men led me to James Traeger, the co-developer of the Navigator programme. We met, talked, got on well and, on the basis that you do not know how something like this will perform until you try it, agreed to pilot the programme at LSE in 1999.

As it was something entirely new, not just to the organisation, but to me as well, I signed up myself as a participant. It was with some trepidation that I joined my peers for the four-day programme, which took place in a rather grand and forbidding board room in our old LSE library.

I still recall the enticing combination of nervous, boyish energy; of authentic engagement and participation; and of candour and good humour as our very mixed group introduced their own life his/stories.

It was immediately apparent that this was both a safe and rather special space, in which it was perfectly possible to ask tough questions and challenge taken-for-granted assumptions whilst never doubting the absolute trust of, and support from, the group.

Lest the false impression be given that Navigator is a kind of collective light-touch lads love-in, it is also worth emphasising the focus, rigour and directed-ness of the experience. This actively encouraged wide-ranging reflection on the way we present and project ourselves, allowed for deeply honest feedback and stimulated clear planning and goal setting. At work and beyond.

This is, in large part, due to the coverage and scope of the Navigator workbook, which successfully walks the tightrope between accessibility and authoritativeness, offering a club mix of ideas, stories, handy hints, theory and practical exercises. As such, it operated not just as a traditional textbook, but rather offered something more robust and coherent, which differentiated it from good periodical journalism, for example. It quite literally guaranteed a well-thumbed copy, engaging and enduring read.

The overall sense was of a worthwhile and distinctive reflective experience, which owed something definite and distinctive to the group male-ness, although my initial sense was to downplay and even deny this at the outset. It may be that my own contemporaneous life experiences at the time – acquiring a wife, mortgage, 'grown up job' and new son – were particularly telling. My sense, however, is that this is only part of the story, and underplays its impact, my general view being that Navigator operated over and above these particularistic variables to reach out and extend to a wide range of ages, ethnicities and work roles struggling to make sense of their take on being a late C20th man.

Navigator continues to offer a worthwhile dialogue for a new generation of C21st men trying to make sense of their roles and responsibilities in an age which further challenges male stereotypes, and sees many work areas in organisations like this become still more heavily female focused.

I warmly welcome this new edition of the workbook and encourage all of you, whatever your specific situation, to enjoy the discussion and engage in the Navigator journey. Be assured you will get a lot out of it.

Chris Connelley
Head, Staff Development Unit
London School of Economics and Political Science

February 2006

Note to the new edition

When I was updating the Navigator workbook for the new edition in 2005, I found myself wondering how much things had really changed between 1996, when we started the whole project, and now, almost a decade on. In particular, I wondered whether much has changed for men. When considering some of the key statistics around work-life balance and so on, I felt uncomfortable that in broad statistical terms, things hadn't moved on all that much for men, or for women.

And yet there has been a shift; I pictured the faces of five thousand men who have been through the Navigator programme in that time, at the edge of a broader trend. I considered all the changes we have witnessed them making, for their own benefit and for the benefit of their families, their communities and their employers. These were sometimes small changes, subtle but significant adjustments that matter for change to be sustainable. I had a sense of a margin that was really moving and changing; a remarkable, if quiet, revolution. I am proud of these men, who continue to defy the stereotype. I celebrate Navigator's part in this tremendously important transition, towards men representing a sense of masculinity which allows them to care for themselves, each other, their communities and the wider world we all share.

James Traeger, Summer 2005

1

Getting Started

Objectives
- To get you started on the *Navigator* programme
- To show you how it might work
- To introduce you to the subject matter
- To get you on the best route for you

This chapter is important because
- You discover the opportunities that this programme offers you
- You get a chance to make some space for it
- You can use a map to plan your route

Content
- Getting started
- Why development and why personal?
- How Navigator works
- Choosing your route

> *If you always do what you've always done then you'll always get what you've always got.*

Getting started

By opening this first page you have decided to take a great opportunity and be positive about yourself, about your life and the future. You have made another fresh start. Congratulations! You are now one of a growing number of men for whom personal development is becoming a vital and practical life skill. Since the Navigator Programme began in 1999, thousands of men have benefited from it.

This chapter tells you about the workbook and how to use it. It explains the benefits to you of working with *Navigator,* looks at how the world is changing for men, and gives you the opportunity to check out how these changes, and change generally, impact on your life.

The *Navigator* programme is a golden opportunity to:

- Assess yourself realistically
- Get support from others
- Learn from your own and others' past experience
- Develop your skills
- Set realistic and challenging goals
- Reach these goals using a strategy
- Become more effective in your work and your personal life
- Move positively into the future
- Focus on what you're good at rather than on past mistakes

Navigator is about developing positive attitudes and skills, in a practical, down-to-earth way. In order for this to happen, *Navigator:*

- Is about making changes
- Is about developing yourself as a whole person, not just the role you play at work or at home.
- Will challenge you to motivate yourself and see this process through to the end
- Will require energy and enthusiasm from you.
- Can be approached on many different levels, according to your need
- Is about you taking responsibility for yourself
- Is about you developing respect for yourself and others with different backgrounds, experiences, attitudes and skills to you
- Doesn't contain any magic answers – only your answers
- Is all about practical action

This workbook is about what you can do to make a difference in your own life. It is not about what your family can do for you, or what the government, your partner, your manager or your employer can do. It is about what you can and will do differently for your own benefit and for the benefit of those you care about.

This is a rare opportunity. Not many men want the chance to set aside time to think about themselves and make positive changes in their lives. You may have decided to do this for yourself, or your employer, or someone else may have encouraged you to get involved.

Whichever it is, giving yourself a chance and making the most of it can open up a whole new world for you.

Why development and why personal?

You have large amounts of skill, talent and potential. If you are committed to discovering them this will be a personal opportunity for you to develop in all aspects of your life. *Navigator* is a programme which will help you find these talents and skills and actively build them.

The development of you as a whole person is more important than ever: the world is changing faster than in previous generations so that almost nothing is fixed or certain – whether at work, home or in the world. The emphasis is now more on each of us setting our own targets, realising our dreams, providing our own job security and direction. Those around us will expect us to take this responsibility for ourselves, rather than wait for them to happen.

Navigator offers the skills, the methods, and the support of men to realise these hopes and dreams – to make our lives enjoyable and forward-looking.

Why just for men?

Men and women can look at their development together, but, as their expectations and motives can be different, there are questions and issues which they also need to answer for themselves.

There can also be a quality of support which men can get from men, women from women – which can particularly help us in our development. This is why *Navigator* and *Springboard* are programmes which complement each other well, by recognising some of the different experiences, ideas and needs of men and of women.

There has been a long, proud tradition of women's development. In these times of massive change it is now more important than ever that men develop resources for men. This approach is deliberately pro-men, as well as supporting development for women.

Men face huge change in every area:

- In the workplace – where there are few jobs for life and a constant need to develop new skills
- In the family – where men's traditional family role as absent breadwinner seems less appropriate
- In our relationships – where communication (a feminine skill?) is more necessary than ever
- In the world generally – where questions are being asked about the future of traditional roles of men and women
- In health – where many men feel the stresses of life

This is the challenge. If men don't rise positively to this challenge, together, they will be blown along by it rather than participating in and directing it according to their aims and objectives. Men deserve a programme that supports them in making the changes they choose, in their way.

How Navigator works

Navigator starts by accepting you as you are while recognising that in a world that is always on the move the people who cope best are those who learn quickly. What is certain is that the more effort you put in, the more reward you will get out. Sometimes, even a relatively small amount of initial effort can have far-reaching consequences in your life.

When you think about how your life has been up to now and how you are feeling about yourself now, you have a choice. You can look at all the areas where life has not gone so well and where you would like to have achieved more, or for things to have been better or different, or you can do the opposite: see the ways in which your life has been a great success story so far and how you are going to make it even better. *Navigator* is about getting a realistic view of where you are now. You can do this yourself with your own efforts and energy and sometimes with the help of your friends, family and work colleagues.

This is a development programme that can be used in lots of different ways. You can approach it superficially or in as much depth as you want. You can do it:

- By yourself
- With the support of one other person
- With a group of men
- Within your workplace

The content and process of this workbook is very broad, to encompass a very wide range of men, at all stages in their lives, from all backgrounds, all levels of ability and disability and with all levels of qualifications.

Personal Development is about thinking in new ways about yourself, developing different types of intelligence. Here are some different intelligences as suggested by (and adapted from) Howard Gardner (Harvard Education School, USA).

EIGHT FORMS OF INTELLIGENCE

Linguistic: sensitivity to spoken and written language, ability to hear languages, and the capacity to use languages to accomplish certain goals;

Logical – mathematical: the capacity to detect patterns, reason deductively and think logically

Musical: skill in the performance, composition and appreciation of musical patterns

Bodily-kinaesthetic: using one's whole body or parts of the body to solve problems

Spatial: the ability to recognise and use the patterns of space and more confined areas

Interpersonal: the capacity to understand the intentions, motivations, and desires of others

Intrapersonal: the capacity to understand oneself, one's feelings, fears and motivations

More recently Gardner has added an eighth form of intelligence:

Naturalist: the ability to recognise, categorise, and draw upon features of the environment, and spirituality/soul quality

Gardner says that multiple intelligences rarely operate independently. They tend to complement each other as people develop skills or solve problems.They develop at different rates and each person has a blend of intelligences that is unique.

Each chapter of the workbook focuses on specific areas of your life and development. It is intended for men who are in paid work, seeking work or in voluntary work, men who are self-employed and men who are prime carers in their homes.

5

When we refer to organisations this could therefore mean the place where you work or hope to work, clubs or societies you belong to, your own business, or you may relate it to your family.

When we refer to partners we mean life partners, male or female, married or not. You could also relate partners to business partners if you have one.

Throughout the workbook there are real examples – extracts, stories and histories, usually anonymous short extracts of other men's lives.

This is your own private workbook, so please feel free to write in the spaces and draw pictures all over it if that helps in your learning. You may want to keep it in a safe place and regard it as a diary, private and confidential.

It is important to ensure you make time available to concentrate on *Navigator,* and also some space of your own where you know you won't be disturbed if you don't want to be. This is important because you will need to be persistent. Distractions will inevitably present themselves, no matter how serious you are at first. Finding time and a private space may be a challenge in itself to some people. You may need to make some changes right from the outset in order to have room in your life for this work on your own development.

Time Put aside two or three hours per week over three months to work through this workbook. This doesn't have to be three solid hours in one go, but at least half an hour in one session is a suggested minimum. Think about:

When are you going to set aside a time?

What are you going to stop doing to make time?

What can you ask others to do to give you some time?

Who or what might hold you back?

What can you do about this?

Place You may need a space where you feel you won't be overlooked so you can concentrate without distraction.

Where can you find somewhere quiet to work?

It is worth putting in the effort to organise the time and space, because that is part of the process of starting or in some cases restarting your journey. With the right environment, it will be a valuable use of time, an activity which you may feel more motivated to keep up. It could be fun too.

Choosing your route

> *The map is not the territory*
>
> Alfred Korsybski

This is a book that you use as you want to use it, and enjoy choosing what you want to look at. You are an adult: the person in the best position to know what the issues are that matter in your own life.

For the rest of your *Navigator* journey you have some choices to make:

- How important specific issues are to you
- In which order you tackle the subjects
- The rest of this chapter helps you make that choice.

The suggestion here is that you do cover all the material but that the order you do it reflects your own choices. The route is up to you.

The following chapters cover a variety of territories:

You need to know about all the chapters because, as your life changes, so different skills will be required in different situations. You might want to flick through the book and glance at all of the chapters so you have a rough idea of what they might cover. Or you may choose to follow your 'gut instinct' (men have intuition too!), choose a topic and dive in.

You can use the map on the next page to plan out where you might like to go. It is very straightforward – just draw a line following the chapter headings to map your route through them. You can start anywhere and finish anywhere.

YOUR PATHWAY AROUND THE CHAPTERS

Your objectives now

This programme is your chance to take three months or so to review your life and revise your priorities. Your overall objectives for *Navigator* may change as you progress; that is a good sign, which shows you are opening up new possibilities. Consider these questions before putting down your overall objectives below, as you embark on this journey:

- Do you have any specific personal or work goals?
- Are you wanting to change your job?
- Are you wanting more time to do the things you do?
- Have you got an overall sense of direction?
- Do you know what you don't want to do?
- What goals do you have for your relationships, at work and outside?
- What might you choose to change about yourself?

What are your objectives as you set out on this journey?
For instance, I want to spend more time with my family
      I want to learn some specific practical skills.

Where do you want to go now?

Think about:
- adding to the notes section, where you can record any useful ideas in the blank pages at the end of the workbook
- deciding which chapter to go to next

Rudy – Birmingham

Past

A successful survivor. Discipline at school. But then changes in environment, in manner. My childhood in Jamaica was happy. When I was 14, I came to England. It was cold. I thought the trees were dead – no leaves. December 1969. Since then, chaos – all upside down.

Present

I've done well, by keeping within what's normal, the law, the system, being a good father, married, my awareness of life. My best characteristic: people tell me I'm a people's man – there's no bad news. My worst – my problem, dyslexia.

Future

Carry on the way I am, hoping to retire back to that nice warm country of mine. A little house, dog in yard, a few fowls, a donkey, a pipe in my mouth, my grandkids. Then my grave, that's it. My life, successful until death.

The Bigger Picture

" *The mind is like a parachute – it works best when it is open* "

The Dalai Lama

Objectives
- To look at the wider issues around development and change
- To look at the world from a different kind of male perspective
- To challenge some stereotypes
- To help you recognise what could change

This chapter is important because
- It can help you to understand change and work with it
- You make your own luck
- You decide what to do in the light of social trends and patterns
- Only you can grasp this opportunity for you
- It helps you be the best you can be by benefiting from the changing role of men

Content
- The bigger picture
- The luck challenge
- Working with change
- A man's world
- Taking responsibility for yourself

Life as a journey

This programme is called *Navigator* because we see life as a journey. Imagine you are about to set sail on a long voyage. You have made many preparations for the journey but you know there are some things that will happen which you can't plan for. You need to be able to adapt as you go. This is what life can be like. You may hit the doldrums where you will drift with no wind for ages, or a tremendous storm may blow you completely off course. Or you may find that you get a really good wind that gets you off to a flying start.

You may find things too hot for you at times and at others you may be in need of warmth. You may end up in a completely new place with different people in your life, different work and new responsibilities. When you think about how far you have come and how much you have achieved you may be pleased, or you may feel frustrated that you are back where you started.

During your life's journey so far, you may have seen many fantastic things and made many decisions. Or you may feel that life has ticked along in quite a humdrum way. In *Navigator,* you will be addressing the whole of your life's journey, and how you can take control and navigate across a sea that may be unpredictable in many ways.

Every person is in certain respects:

- Like all other people
- Like some other people
- Like no other person

In what ways are you like all other people?
For instance, you have a name

In what ways are you like some other people?
For instance, you are a man

In what ways are you like no other people?
For instance, your particular life's events

The luck challenge

Some people say, when asked how they got to where they are, 'I was lucky'. They may feel this is true for them, but with *Navigator* you can learn to make your own luck! If you looked at the lives of most people who have achieved something worthwhile, it is because they have:

- Shown willing
- Participated
- Stuck with it
- Recognised change as an opportunity
- Set themselves goals
- Had some courage
- Made contacts
- Learned new skills of their own accord
- Volunteered

Most people are quite modest and find it hard to take the credit for what they have achieved in their life. It's much easier to say 'I was lucky'. Yet there is no doubt that if you don't try, try and try again, you don't succeed, and when you have succeeded, you deserve the credit for all the effort. Luck does play a part, of course, but perhaps a smaller part than most people are prepared to admit.

Luck happens when preparation meets opportunity

You won't always know when the next opportunity will come along, but if you start preparing now it may come along sooner than you expected.

Working with change

The world is changing very fast, faster than anyone might have imagined twenty years ago, faster than your parents' generation experienced. Being a successful man in today's world means being able to face up to change, look it squarely in the eye and say 'I will work with you'. Many people find this quite a challenge. People respond to challenges in different ways. Some:

13

- See a change as a bad thing, something to fight
- Pretend it's not happening
- Stick their heads in the sand and try to ignore a change for as long as they can
- Insist that the old way is better
- Are wary but prepared to go along with it
- Accept it once they've been persuaded
- Immediately accept it because someone tells them to
- Just love the challenge of change and are disappointed when there is none
- Thrive on change
- Actively seek the challenge of change to make their lives more exciting, interesting or fun.

Which one of the above are you most like?

What can *you* change? It is helpful to recognise that whilst you can't change everything about this journey, there are definitely things you can affect and alter.

While it may be difficult or even impossible to change:

- Where you were born and your family background
- The physical characteristics you have inherited from your parents
- How other people are
- Your past
- How others see you now

You can influence and change:

- How you see yourself and others
- What you care about
- What you can do
- How healthy you are
- How you communicate with people and express yourself
- How you access and express your feelings
- Your current life and work pattern
- How you spend your time and money
- Your future

- Some aspects of your immediate community and occasionally even the world
- How you build relationships at home and at work
- How you let your past affect you

What do you want to change?

You may also have changed because of things that have happened to you: those things for which you couldn't plan. You can't always be responsible for the way the world changes, but you can definitely prepare yourself for change. This preparation is about becoming more aware of how you respond and adapt, as well as making concrete plans.

The great increase in importance of computers and information technology is just one area of change that will affect all people, in every area of life. So is the ability to travel great distances in a relatively short time.

There are of course many different reasons why these sort of changes are happening. Some people say that society is witnessing the biggest changes since the Industrial Revolution, two hundred years ago.

But remember that the reason it is happening is not nearly as important as what are you going to do about it

…and what you do about it will be reflected in all aspects of your life:

If you work (full time, part time, on a voluntary or paid basis), how will you respond to the changes at work?

Or, if you don't work, how will you deal with finding a job?

If you have a life partner, how will you deal with her/his changing work and home role?

If you have children or other close family, what changes do they face in the future?

How do you see your community changing?

However your life goes, there is no doubt that change will be a regular travelling companion on your journey. So ask yourself:

How do you feel about change?

Why might you not like change?

The well-being and change curve

Elizabeth Kübler-Ross developed a model following her research into the way people deal with change. It shows the stages people tend to follow when something changes in their lives. It aims to show how going through change and facing it can increase your capacity. 'Capacity' means your self-esteem, your resilience, your ability to help and support others, even your overall well-being and confidence.

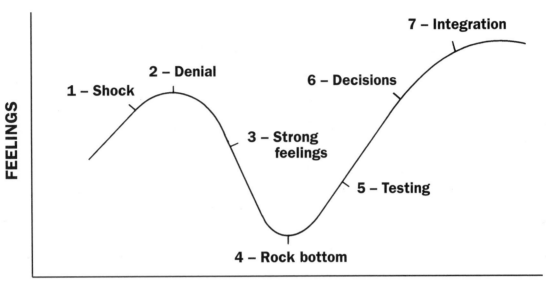

Stage 1 – Shock: In shock we are numb and may not even recognise that change has happened, for example following a major accident or even with the surprise of a lottery win. 'I can't really take it in!'

Stage 2 – Denial: Denial of the change and finding ways to prove that it isn't happening. Sticking your head in the sand and reassuring yourself that it isn't really happening. I'll carry on as before. It has always worked up to now. These new ideas will blow over.

Stage 3 – Strong feelings: On the way down, you may be experiencing feelings such as anger, anxiety and frustration, even if you aren't expressing it. Often there is a tendency to blame everyone else and lash out at them. You may feel annoyed that this is all happening to you and expecting 'them', managers or family and friends, to put it right.

Stage 4 – Rock bottom: You may be hitting rock bottom, feeling low and powerless, maybe even depressed and apathetic. Everything seems pointless and there is no point in doing anything. You may feel like giving up. This is the stage of lowest self-esteem, or capacity. When we reach the lowest point this can motivate us to do something, because we can't go on like this.

Stage 5 – Testing: This is where you start to try out new things. 'It is time to do something. I have to try something. There has to be something better than this. Maybe I'll just try......'

Stage 6 – Decisions: Having tried out some new things, deciding what works and what doesn't. Accepting the change and realising that there is a new way to behave, and be in the change. 'I can see what works for me and I will go on doing that.'

Stage 7 – Integration: The new you. The changes are now part of your life and they feel good to you. Doing things in your new way is now fully integrated into your life.

In this model not everybody goes through these phases in exactly the same way. For some people, the curve is quite shallow, while for others it can be steep. We all have our favourite resting places along the way. Some try out new ideas and if they don't work they go back to being depressed, others leap back to being angry. Do you know where you tend to get stuck? Understanding and working with a model of change is useful, not just in relation to work but in your life generally.

The diagram has an important point. You may notice the curve ends higher than it started, suggesting that, by undergoing change, we can benefit greatly by being more experienced, and having a greater sense of well-being and potential.

THINKING ABOUT HOW YOU WORK WITH CHANGE:

When dealing with change, the things I do well are:

When dealing with change the things that I would like to do better are:

The differences between the way I deal with change at work and outside work are:

Get feedback from someone else. Ask them 'How do I deal with change?'

How does her/his view compare with how you see yourself? Is there a big difference?

Bearing all this section in mind, summarise here your own way of dealing with change, at work and outside of work:

Sometimes you will be in control of change; sometimes it will come quite unexpectedly, or in a way you don't immediately like.

When change comes unexpectedly, you have a choice:

- You can either work in with it, turning it to your advantage, or
- You can resist it to the end, trying to stop its progress or at least slow it down

Think about people who are familiar with the second way. They know how to argue, resist, sabotage and generally make things difficult for new things to happen. Sometimes this may be an appropriate way to act. Sometimes it simply represents a negative and uncooperative way of behaving.

Think about the people you know who tend to be skilled at working with change, at judging the tide of the times and making preparations so that they can take advantage of them. They suggest what to do to make changes work. They bring constructive criticism if there are areas where they think that aspects of the change will not work. They openly express their feelings about what can go well with the change. They also raise their concerns with a view to overcoming them.

You may not always want to work along with change in this way. But at least you will have another option, rather than just resisting it, or just hoping it won't affect you.

Your Circle of Influence

In his popular book *The 7 Habits of Highly Effective People,* Stephen R. Covey talks about a famous Austrian psychologist Victor Frankl, who survived the experience of a Nazi Concentration camp in the Second World War. Covey says that Frankl did this by realising that he was in control of his own attitude, feelings and emotions, in fact his own mind, no matter what other people did to him.

Covey describes this in a picture, which he calls the Circle of Concern/Circle of Influence:

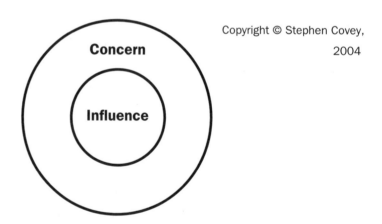

Copyright © Stephen Covey, 2004

The larger of the two circles covers all your 'concerns': all the things in your life that bother you, or that are simply on your mind. The smaller circle inside this depicts all the things in your life that you think you have some control over.

Covey says that Frankl survived because of his attitude and that with this same attitude you can survive, and even thrive, in today's chaotic world. This means putting your energy into the things that you have some influence over, rather than those things that bother you but that you don't think you can do anything about. This means focusing on the circle of influence rather than your circle of concern beyond it. This doesn't mean you stop being bothered by the things in the larger circle, just that you realise that this may not be a good use of your focus and thinking power.

For example, if the organisation in which you work is going through another big change, rather than worrying about it and about what sort of decisions are going to be made by others, and not by you, focus your thinking on the opportunities that are appearing, or may yet appear for you as a result of this change, even if they are unexpected.

This shift of thinking marks the people who can survive and do well in a quickly changing world. It also shows us that the people who find modern life stressful are usually the ones who feel that most things are happening 'to them' beyond their own control. The more you can focus on your circle of influence, therefore, the more in control and less stressed you may feel. Try it and see what happens.

A man's world

The manifesto below[1] makes important and interesting statements, but some reservations by John Rowan are also cited (in brackets), to temper some of the more extreme positions:

THE NEW MALE MANIFESTO

1. Men are beautiful. Masculinity is life-affirming and life-supporting. Male sexuality generates life. The male body needs and deserves to be nurtured and protected. *[A bit one-sided, but manifestos are like that. Men are beautiful and ugly, fascinating and boring, mature and childish, positive and negative....]*

2. A man's value is not measured by what he produces. We are not merely our professions. We need to be loved for who we are. We make money to support life. Our real challenge, and adventure that makes life full, is making soul. *[Again a bit partial, but worth stating as a counterbalance to the usual doctrine.]*

3. Men are not flawed by nature. We become destructive when our masculinity is damaged. Violence springs from desperation and fear rather than authentic manhood. *[That is certainly worth saying.]*

---

4. A man doesn't have to live up to any narrow, societal image of manhood. There are many ancient images of men as healers, protectors, lovers, and partners with women, men, and nature. This is how we are in our depths: celebrators of life, ethical and strong. *[This is where the Horned God, the Green Man, comes in as an exemplar.]*

5. Men do not need to become more like women in order to reconnect with soul. Women can help by giving men room to change, grow, and rediscover masculine depth. Women also support men's healing by seeking out and affirming the good in them. *[Some very important points here; there is persistent confusion about 'developing our feminine side' and so forth, which this book tries to clarify.]*

6. Masculinity does not require denial of deep feeling. Men have the right to express all their feelings. In our society this takes courage and the support of others. We start to die when we are afraid to say or act upon what we feel. *[Not quite right here: male expression of feelings can be quite frightening at times, and quite overbearing on others. It is not a question of giving carte blanche to men to cultivate their feelings at the expense of others, but rather a question of expanding the range of our feelings in appropriate ways.]*

7. Men are not only competitors. Men are also brothers. It is natural for us to co-operate and support each other. We find strength and healing through telling the truth to one another – man to man. *[This is worth saying, but misses the point about co-creation as a third choice, which my own work tries to make.]*

8. Men deserve the same rights as women for custody of children, economic support, government aid, education, health care, and protection from abuse. Fathers are equal to mothers in their ability to raise children. Fatherhood is honourable. *[On slightly dangerous territory here: it sounds alright at first, but ignores the points about power which Bob Connell makes, and assumes a level playing field.]*

9. Men and women can be equal partners. As men learn to treat women more fairly they also want women to work toward a vision of partnership that does not require men to become less than who they authentically are. *[Similar reservations here; we can't be equal in a culture of inequality, and until the culture changes equality may be impossible. It is not just an individual matter.]*

10. Sometimes we have the right to be wrong, irresponsible, unpredictable, silly, inconsistent, afraid, indecisive, experimental, insecure, visionary, lustful, lazy, fat, bald, old, playful, fierce, irreverent, magical, wild, impractical, unconventional, and other things we're not supposed to be in a culture that circumscribes our lives with rigid roles. *[I agree.]*

In many ways, men may feel victims of some bad press. There are many beliefs about men: for instance, that they are competitive, aggressive, uncommunicative, inflexible, unemotional, perpetrators of the most crimes... etc. etc. But how true is this for you? Is it perhaps true that men are so used to playing up to these stereotypes that they themselves believe in them?

As a man, you may act the role that is expected of you, but inside you may know you are as co-operative, peaceful, sociable, open-minded and intuitive as the next man. And these latter qualities are exactly those in demand for employable and happy people of the future. Men have got these qualities – you have got them – you just need to tell others about them,

Many assumptions can be made about men, learning and organisations.

Check out on this list:

What rings true (✔) what is totally untrue (✘) What raises questions (?)

MEN...

...OR ARE THEY?

MEN...	...OR ARE THEY?
Are all the same under the skin	Unique individuals
Are confused about who they are	Aware of their multi-faceted identity
Are out of touch, uncomfortable with their feelings	Passionate, loving, vulnerable, intuitive, wise
Want to control, compete, have power over others	Cooperative, committed to service and stewardship
Struggle for scarce resources	Willing to share resources in an abundant world
Are oppressive and fearful of diversity and change	Self-motivating, open-minded, accepting of others
Are unable to support themselves and each other	Capable of powerful support for self and others
Are blown about by the forces of destiny	Able to set their own goals and devise a clear strategy
Are losing the gender war	World-building on an equal footing with women

23

The bigger picture of work and home

Looking at the bigger picture in the worlds of work and home in the UK: [2]

- Men and women born in 2002 could expect to live to 76 and 81 years of age respectively, in contrast to 1901 when men could expect to reach 45 and women 49.
- The pattern of partnership formation has changed in the last 30 years. The proportion of married people has fallen, while the proportion of single and divorced people has increased (1.5 million divorced men in 2001, compared to 187,000 in 1971)
- 6% of households with children are lone parented in 2001, compared to 3% in 1971
- 10% of lone parent households were headed by a lone father in 2002
- The percentage of men active in the workforce has dropped from 60 to 50% in the last 20 years.
- 2.8 million fewer and 2 million more women have been in the active workforce in the last 20 years.
- There will be more women than men in work during the 21st Century if current trends continue.
- Men seem to be consistently reluctant to take the lower-paid, more flexible working options that are putting more women into work.
- 66% of working-age women work, despite earning 72% of men's average wage.
- Girls are tending to perform better than boys at school – for example with less truancy and expulsion. In 1996, there were 1,177 boys under 11 years old expelled or excluded from school in England and Wales, compared with only 91 girls. One theory about why boys might not be performing so well is that they do not get as much contact with older male role models as girls do with the female equivalent.
- There has been huge growth in the numbers of men involved in diverse leisure activities of all kinds, from DIY to yoga to rock climbing to community voluntary work.
- In 2005 men in the UK are doing twice as much housework as in 1961, amounting to an average of 146 minutes per day. This includes cooking, washing up, shopping and childcare. But women still do twice as much on average as men.
- On average men spend 16 minutes per day on childcare in 2005, compared to 3 minutes in 1961.

Overall the picture is as follows: the labour market is increasingly friendly to women (though men still make more money and are more likely to be in work) but there are growing numbers of men outside the labour market in a way that women have been accustomed but men are not. Women tend to be better educated; they stay longer in jobs (especially women with children); low-paid jobs are growing more quickly and women are readier to accept them than men, who still see themselves as a family's breadwinner; women tend to have the social skills needed for a job in services.

The Economist

So many of the old certainties are gone. The old saying that this was 'a man's world' may now be an unhelpful attitude, and anyway, many men do not feel that this is so, at least not any more. At work, although there is no doubt that men are economically and politically still very much in the majority at the top of the status- and pay-pyramid, this situation is changing in the UK, in a way that is felt by the great majority in the wider base of work status and pay roles.

Although men still have more of the highest status/pay jobs and fewer of lowest status/pay jobs than women, the middle ground is where women are gaining a bigger role, while still being more willing to take on the lower-paid, lower status jobs.

The Work Status and Pay Pyramid

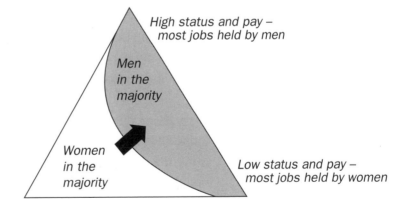

Looking at this diagram, what do you think is ideal?

- Should it be half and half, with exactly the same number of men and women employed at every level?
- Or is there a natural tendency to divide in some other way?

You need to have a view on this because it is the sort of question facing all men and women now and in the future.

Relationships between men and women have also changed. The traditional idea that women have to find a man in order to provide for themselves and their families is no longer valid – more and more women are setting themselves up in economic independence. Although people still talk about career women (and never career men), it is no longer easy to say what is a man's job and what is a woman's job. At home the roles are becoming less distinct. Some men are choosing to stay at home more, look after the kids and, although still quite rarely, even do the housework.

All this will have an effect on your life in some way – either directly because you have experienced these changes first hand, or indirectly, because it will be affecting people you know, or society's attitudes and expectations of you.

Whether these changes are good or bad is not the point here, even if it makes for a good TV chat show or pub debate. What matters here is:

How will you respond positively to what is happening?

Although some people choose to look at the ever-changing world as a gloomy prospect, *Navigator* offers to help you see this as a positive opportunity, if you are willing to take on the challenge. Increasingly it is not men or women who are favoured by society, but *people,* the *individuals* with the positive attitude and relevant skills, irrespective of their gender, race, age, sexual orientation, spiritual or philosophical background or physical ability. This means that you will be judged, alongside everyone else, by what you can do, your skills and abilities and perhaps more importantly, how you put these across.

What are men like?

Men, as much as anyone else, need to look at themselves, as individuals and as a group, if they are to develop these positive attitudes and skills. Some argue that men are less capable of doing this, especially together. Some people say that men can't be supportive and caring. They say that men are more competitive, aggressive and uncaring towards their fellow human beings, all qualities which will be increasingly less advantageous. They also say that men 'behave badly and should be more like women in order to stay in the race'.

You might think that men *can* be cooperative, caring, supportive, even nurturing towards each other and others, in *their* way, and this doesn't necessarily mean they are being more like women. You might think men aren't necessarily worse at these things than women.

For everyone it is important to have a life outside work: not just interests and hobbies but activities to which you may be committed, something you care about, something for which you are prepared to give up evenings or weekends.

Is this so? If you were to generalise, what do you think men are like?

In what ways are you similar to this generalisation?

In what ways are you different from this?

Men and their anoraks

Sometimes men pursuing such activities get a bad press, and have become known variously as 'anoraks',' geeks', 'bores', 'fans', 'fanatics' or 'nerds'.

The stereotypical anorak is supposedly:

- A train spotter
- Has his woolly hat with railway badges on it, as well as his anorak, and checked trousers
- Has binoculars and his railway timetable to hand

This clichéd image is not one, of course, that most men would like to think is anything or anybody like them. So if they are not like this, here is a broader definition: An anorak has four main characteristics:

1 **Passionate** – he doesn't just like football, aeroplanes, local history or whatever it is, but has a passion about it, cares about what goes on with it, and wants to share his interest with others.

2   **Commitment to detail** – the particular history of his team, the specific beer he knows and loves are important. To others who do not share his interest this detail seems strange if not weird: how can it be worth arguing for half an hour about whether a particular striker would have won us the World Cup semi-finals in 1990 if he hadn't been booked? But to him it is important.

3   **Enthusiastic** – he enjoys his subject, he pursues it because it interests and motivates him.

4   **Voluntary** – the anorak is interested in his subject, not because it's part of his job, or he gets paid for it. Sometimes he does get paid as well: the point is that payment is not the main motivation for pursuing the subject.

It is the combination of all four of these characteristics that distinguishes being an 'anorak' from a chosen pursuit being just a hobby.

Most people agree that anoraks can be women as well as men: if you need any proof go down to a traditional Church and talk to the bell-ringers. The chances are that most of them will be women and many might be quite happy to describe themselves as anoraks. However, the stereotype is of a man, and certainly if you go to air shows or steam-train rallies you will see far more men there than women. But do women wear their anoraks differently? Do we men pursue our passions on our own, whereas women tend to pursue theirs as a group?

Whether men or women, the world needs anoraks. Many voluntary organisations could not survive without the dedication and commitment of its anorak members. Without them historic buildings would not be saved and preserved, whole aspects of our culture ranging from local cricket clubs to bird-spotter societies would not exist, and the country would be considerably poorer.

Yet there are potentially negative aspects of being an anorak, which it is important to be aware of.

> *My 10 year-old-daughter told me once that she always gets a headache whenever I go with her to the City of London, such is my enthusiasm to show her the dragons all around the boundary, the Bank of England, the Mansion House, where I got my City Guide badge from the Lord Mayor and so on.*
>
> Hugh Dennis

Anoraks can be obsessed, even fanatical, with their subject, and therefore do not see it or themselves in proper perspective. Pursuing it in a single-minded way can make them more isolated and/or mean that they try to prove themselves to others, taking on the persona of the 'clever-dick'. As with much of the material in this workbook, it is important to keep things in perspective.

But in general, being an anorak is nothing to be ashamed of; it is something to be celebrated, enjoyed and studied, not apologised for. One way we can do this is to meet with other anoraks; being an anorak is often at its best with others. In this way we can celebrate both our pursuits and the fact that, as men, we do them well. Wear your anorak with pride!

What does society expect from men today?

So far in *Navigator* you've been thinking about how your life is and what you can take responsibility for. Whilst doing this, it will be useful to consider how the world has changed for men generally, and what is expected of them now that we have entered the new millennium.

People recognise:

- The certainties of the past are gone
- There is no such thing as a job for life anymore
- Most people will face unemployment at some time in their working life
- New uncertainties are emerging

If men see themselves and their identities only in terms of what they do to 'earn a crust' for their families, how will these changes affect their health, their self-esteem, or the expectations of young men and boys starting out in life?

It may seem that the world has changed so much that a completely new and different approach is needed. Or it may be that some things never seem to change. Making sense of all of this for yourself can clarify the influences that have shaped you to be the man you are.

The following men offer their stories about how the world has changed between previous generations and their own.

John – Staffordshire

I think my father's world of work was very different from mine. This has something to do with our unique characters, but I have recently become more aware of the differences created by the generation gap, and of how values have changed within organisations. My father left school and got an excellent apprenticeship in a large engineering company, which included sending him on part-time education programmes to get his vocational qualifications. He now has more letters after his name than I can recall, all of them engineering-based, and he hasn't been to university.

During my father's 30-odd years with one company, it appeared that he missed out on a lot of perks, one example being that each time he was promoted, they moved the management grading required for a company car one level higher.

At the age of 53, my father's loyal service ended in redundancy. Against all the odds, he walked straight into a new position with a firm of consultants, working better hours, doing more interesting work, getting paid more and he finally got a company car. Now at 65, he does not want to retire and he has negotiated with his employer to work part-time.

I, like many sons, followed my father into engineering, but not an apprenticeship with a large company. I lasted 2 terms full time at a Technical College, and left before they kicked me out.

At the age of 21, with nothing but 5 'O' levels, I had an office-based job with a company car. New opportunities within the organisation were being offered to me as quickly as I could say, 'Yes, thank you.' At the age of 25, I was earning the same as my father, without any formal qualifications.

Since then I have participated in several careers, and I am still doing a variety of roles, all of them on a self-employed basis. Depending on what week or month it is, I am a management trainer, a carpenter, a farm worker and a Landrover mechanic – and I love the variety.

Of course, when I started out, I thought I'd be working for the same company for 30 years, just like my dad. Today we are both fortunate enough to have sufficient variety in our work to keep us mentally and emotionally stimulated, though our routes to the same end have been divergent.

Steve – Yorkshire

Thoughts about differences between mine and my father's generation...

Dad was a great aviator with his Airfix construction sets, and I was a great director with my Super 8mm movies (he never flew a plane and I never directed a movie – except in our dreams).

Dad travelled abroad with the army in World War II and met hostile enemy soldiers, and I travelled abroad in peace time and met friendly local people (same country).

Dad liked Vera Lynn, Shirley Bassey, Harry Secombe, and I liked Francoise Hardy, Sparks and Kate Bush (come to think of it I quite liked Shirley too).

Dad was into his Church and reading about theology, and I was into my cinema and reading about films (both involve looking at something that's not really there).

Dad married his girl and had two children, but I couldn't marry my man and have kids (it didn't stop me from being as happy as he was though).

Dad worked in a gelatine factory most of his life, and I worked in the education factory most of mine (both forming raw materials into something useful).

Dad was always there for me and did his best for me, and I hope I'm always there for him now (I still ask him how to make things grow).

Colin – Wales

My father ended up doing a job that was not right for him so as to feed his family. I am not sure whether he resented it or not. I have far more choice in what I do. I have many friendships with women which I don't think my father would have had. My parents had joint friends really, whereas my partner and I have some individual friends and some joint friends.

In his relationships I don't think my father and friends would talk as much about what was going on in their lives or what they were feeling as I do with my friends. My Dad had two very happy relationships with his wives (he remarried after my Mum died young). My interests are largely similar to my Dad's – sport, arts, literature. The big difference though is my interest in personal development. He definitely came from a 'keep it all inside' and 'don't show emotion' age and culture, and found it very difficult to understand (although he tried) what it was I was doing, when I talked to him about personal development stuff – it was all really a foreign concept to him.

Although in later years he did try a bit, my father knew hardly anything about domestic matters. This comes partly from his age and partly age combined with class – being brought up as an upper class man in the 1910s, 20s and 30s, it was not his mother who did all the work but the maid, cook and nanny. Nevertheless, as a courteous man he always offered to help and would do the washing up.

I have a far more central role in domestic chores. This is not only my choice but also my partner's expectation. For my mother, any help my father gave around the house was a bonus!

He lived in a far more ordered world, in the sense that he liked routine. He couldn't understand why things had suddenly changed so much – both technologically but even more so in the way people thought – for example, feminism he did not really understand at all. He and his friends hankered for the certainties of the world they had grown up with. His lifestyle was ordered too. Work, time with family, hobbies, time with friends. It seems to me that he felt he had a lot less choice in his life than I feel I have and that his life changed a lot less than mine has in terms of interests, friends, career. Although there were some changes, the core of his life remained the same for 50 years. I am not sure he would have chosen to change it (perhaps he just knew what he liked), but I think he didn't believe he had a choice.

My Dad settled for what life gave him, and focused on the family that was his main pleasure. I don't think he expected fulfilment in work or in other ways. It was just nice when he could take a bit of time for himself and do the things that he enjoyed doing but this was more about leisure than fulfilment. He was not religious either. I tend to look far more for purpose and fulfilment in all aspects of my life. In this way, he was perhaps a lot more accepting than I am.

Don – Oxfordshire

1. Life is now so much more challenging than it was for my father.

His role was that of the traditional breadwinner. He did virtually none of the household chores, but wasn't expected to. He had limited involvement in the bringing up of my brother and me. He did the man's jobs and my mother did the woman's jobs and there was little overlap.

My son, however, has different responsibilities. He has to play his part in the daily household maintenance, as well as cook, as well as iron – as well as hold down a demanding job in the IT industry. When his child is born next month he will be expected to play a much greater part in the nurturing process: feeding, nappy changing, eventually school runs, etc – a fully comprehensive fathering role.

2. Today, expectations are higher – fulfilment may be lower.

Life has so much more to offer now than in my father's time. He would be amazed by the choice available in clothing, cars, financial services, DIY materials, entertainment, holidays, leisure/sporting pursuits, eating out, etc.

Paradoxically, my son may feel frustrated because he can only tap a small proportion of this potential – he cannot take advantage of nearly as much as he would ideally like to. My father had a much higher hit rate on a much lower portfolio of opportunity and was probably more content as a result.

I call this the motorway café syndrome. What is more satisfying? Going into a restaurant and, from a very limited menu, finding a dish that is just right for you? Or, being faced with a menu that has so many dishes you would like to select that, when the meal is served, you spend half your time looking at others' choices and wishing you could have tried theirs too.

From *High Fidelity* by Nick Hornby

I'm happy to be a bloke, I think, but sometimes I'm not happy being a bloke in the late twentieth century. Sometimes I'd rather be my dad. He never had to worry about delivering the goods, because he never knew there were any goods to deliver; he never had to worry how he ranked in my mother's all-time one hundred, because he was first and last on the list. Wouldn't it be great if you could talk about this sort of thing to your father?

To generalise, young men **in the past** in the western world were told:

- It's a man's world, as long as you're the right kind of man
- Stability and life-long loyalty to one employer are important
- Work and home are completely separate
- A woman's place is at home, a man's is at work
- In any divorce or separation the children will probably end up with their mother
- Women work until they get pregnant and never go seriously back to their career
- A woman's job is never as important as her partner's
- Don't have feelings – 'big boys don't cry'
- Know your place, depending on your race, class, age, background, ability

Add your recollections

How does this compare with a generalised picture of **today's western world:**

- It's anybody's game
- Be prepared to start a new career several times in your life, often with different employers
- There is no clear distinction between the skills needed inside and outside work

- There is no such thing as men's work and women's work
- A woman's job may be more breadwinning than her partner's
- A man has just as much right to be with his children and perform a caring role as a woman
- Diverse lifestyles, partnerships, separations and relationships of many types exist in society
- Men can be single parents just as effectively as women
- Having a family and working are two sides of the same coin
- Expect to become unemployed at some point – use it as an opportunity to re-energise your life
- The way you do it is as important as what you do
- You can be any kind of man you want to be

In this light what advice would you give to younger men?

In 2002, Sonderman[3] defined the **11 Important Needs of Men**:

- Action
- Safety
- To be challenged
- To get to the point
- To win
- To dream
- Other men like them
- Help working around daily work
- Healing
- Freedom
- To identify

Taking responsibility for yourself

In other words, are you a participant in life or someone who watches life go by? It may be that you sit back and pass comment on the world and the lives of others, as a passive observer. Or are you more of a participant in life, prepared to stick your neck out and say, 'This is my life and I'm going to live it to the full'? Life for many is a balancing act between observing and doing.

Taking responsibility for yourself means your whole self. This means learning about yourself, not just what you think or what facts and figures you know. It is a much wider question, which means you need to consider:

- How you see yourself
- What your life experience has been
- How you feel
- How you express your feelings
- The impact of your background and the community you come from
- What really matters to you and motivates you for the future
- Your helpful and unhelpful attitudes and ways of acting
- Your creativity
- Your sensitivity to others
- Your hopes, expectations and vision
- The relationship between your mind, body, soul or spirit
- Taking action towards a chosen future
- What you do and its impact on others

And more.

What areas of your life do you think you can take more responsibility for?

- *In your work:* For instance, joining a project group

- *At home:* For instance, doing more around the house

– *In your relationships:* For instance, spending more time with my daughter

– *On your own/for yourself:* For instance, doing something new I've always wanted to do

Taking responsibility for yourself and showing respect is not about agreeing or disagreeing with everybody else. It has nothing to do with attitudes or opinions. It is almost what could be called a human right – the space to give yourself and someone else the time of day, even (or especially) when they are quite a different sort of person to you.

Taking responsibility for yourself is also about asking for help when you need it and not trying to bravely soldier on, if you don't have to.

In this workbook a large part of taking responsibility for yourself will be directed at realistic self-assessment. You have to be able to know what it is you can and can't do, realistically, without kidding yourself. The better able you are to self-assess realistically, the more chance you have of finding your niche in life, and building good relationships at work and at home. You can both sell yourself on the basis of your true abilities and identify clearly what new skills you want to develop. With the ability to take stock of yourself realistically and the will to get on, you can achieve almost anything.

Where do you want to go now?

Think about:
– adding to the notes section, where you can record any useful ideas in the blank pages at the end of the workbook
– deciding which chapter to go to next

Stephen – Merseyside

Past

I grew up in a stable, loving, working class family. I enjoyed my school years, though maybe too much to work hard enough and go on to a further education.

Present

I feel now that part of my job is done; my children have grown up and I am now enjoying some more freedom. My best quality is that I am consistent – I get on with most people, and my worst is that I can be passive.

Future

I don't have many ambitions, but I will always try to take advantage of any situation, at work or outside – I have 'gone for it' before and will do again. I just want my two children to think that for all the ups and downs there have been, I always had their interests at heart. I like to describe myself as a 'millionaire without the money'!

3

Who are You?

" We don't see things as they are, we see things as we are "

The Talmud

Objective
- To clarify what is important in your life, how you see yourself and how this compares with how others see you

This chapter is important because
- Investigating who you are is a starting point for your journey
- How you see yourself may be different to how others see you
- This difference may be a clue to your values, attitudes and prejudices
- Being clear about what matters to you will help you achieve your objectives

Content
- Your values
- Your identity
- Celebrating diversity and overcoming prejudice
- Your attitudes
- Superman or supermen?

Who are you?

This is a simple question, which opens up a whole range of issues to do with your identity, that is, how you see yourself, what matters to you and how that fits in with how others see you.

Your values

Who you are is also about what values you have – in other words, what's important to you, what motivates you and what shapes your view of the world. Your values are reflected in your attitudes and beliefs. This chapter clarifies your scheme of values.

What you value decides what makes sense to you. Logic and reason are determined by what you value. You may not think two plus two can ever add up to anything except four, but for example, if someone's life is at stake, then anything becomes possible. If a life raft has only four places in it and there are five of you needing rescue, then you may try to squeeze five into four. That is because life is valuable to you. It is useful to identify which of your values are not being met, as this can open up a goal area – something you can aim for.

Work – an important male value forever?

Before you consider your value system, consider work as a value in itself. For most men work is an essential part of their identity, a crucial value. Yet, what happens to a man who is unemployed? It may affect his self-esteem very deeply, especially if what he does for a living is an important part of his identity. Yet it is quite likely that most men (and women) will face unemployment at least once in their career.

And what happens to a man's sense of himself if his partner becomes the major breadwinner? Can being a house-husband become part of a man's identity? Will 'keeping a tidy home with a clean kitchen' become an important male value? Although this may not be an important value for you quite yet, you could think about how important to you paid work is, in terms of your sense of self.

⌐ *If you work, why do you work?*

⌐ *If you had a large private income, would you still choose to work full-time?*

What else might you do more of instead of working full-time?

What might stop you from doing this?

If you don't work, how do you feel about it?

> **You can never afford to have children**   Anon

Your value system   You are making choices and decisions about your life all the time:

- In the way you choose to behave
- In the way you choose to respond or react to situations
- In the priorities you place on relationships, home life and activities
- In the way you spend your money
- In the way you divide your time between work and other things
- In the way you relate to the rest of the world
- In the way you feel and think about yourself

These choices reflect what you value. Even if you aren't aware of making these choices, you are showing what you value by what you don't choose to do. You have power in terms of what you value, whether you are aware of it or not, and you are exercising that power almost all the time. If you consider what you value, and get clear about this, then you can also be clear about where to go next, or at the very least where you can avoid ending up.

41

Paying attention to your values will also help you manage stress:

- When you feel like your values are being met, you may be more motivated and content. Your stress level may be about right.
- When you feel like your values aren't being met, you may feel dissatisfied and lacking in energy. You may feel more stressed than is comfortable.

This applies especially when the values in question are currently your most important ones. Keeping on target with your priority values will help you manage your stress level.

Your values do not stay the same forever but change with time. Most people start off with their parents' or community's value system and many rebel against this during adolescence. However, as you get older, you may recognise the values and priorities learned from your parents changing, for example, when you become a parent yourself or approach retirement age.

It is not always easy to balance the different things we value. Balancing 'earning a good living' may seem incompatible with 'spending time at home with my kids' for some men. This is where the choices come in and you ask further questions, such as how much is a 'good living'? And 'when they are older, what are they going to remember: the things I bought for them or the time I spent with them?'

Values relate to four different areas of your life: world, work, relationships and self. These four areas overlap and sometimes they can clash – for example, you want a car because you value independence for yourself, but you also value a pollution-free world. These are the dilemmas you navigate all the time, and they come from your system of values.

World/community

For instance,

    the right to vote

    a peaceful world

    a prosperous local community

    something beautiful outside my front door

    a healthy mental and physical environment

Work

For instance,

    money

    challenge

    promotion

    team working

    perks

Relationships

For instance,

    someone special

    time with children

    stability

    sense of humour

    to be understood and accepted

For yourself

For instance,

    time for quiet contemplation

    time out with friends

    clothes, car, material things

    space for my own interests

    holiday more than once a year

    spirituality

What do you value?   What matters to you? What is important? What do you value?

Write down all the things you can think of that you value in these four categories:

For the world:

At work:

In your relationships:

For yourself:

Prioritise your values according to this chart:

	1st priority: **I MUST have:**	2nd priority: **I would like to have:**	3rd priority: **It would be nice to have:**
World/ community			
Work			
Relationships			
Myself			

Now tick the values on this chart that are being met at the moment, and underline the ones that are not being met.

What other surprises were there about your chart, if any?

How do you feel about your unfulfilled values?

Which unfulfilled values do you want to do something about?

Making changes in order to meet particular values can become an important objective for you in *Navigator.*

If you had a number of values in the 'I must have' or 'I would like to have' sections of the above chart that aren't being met, then this exercise has opened up some important opportunities for you. These can become goal areas, which you can address in Chapter 5 – Setting Goals.

You can choose to respond to your unfulfilled values in a variety of ways, for example by:
- Gaining the drive and determination to do something about it
- Becoming bitter and cynical
- Daydreaming wistfully about what life might have been
- Complaining that life isn't fair
- Realising that you can't accept responsibility for everything in the world, all at once
- Becoming more aware of how you give away your power to make choices in your life
- Finding some support to make a change

How you respond is up to you, but personal development itself is underpinned by the value that you CAN make changes in these areas of your life.

Your identity

The meaning of your name

The short answer to the question: Who are you? is your name. A name has meaning. It immediately tells a story about who you are. You can use this to your advantage. Even if your name is a relatively commonplace one, it still has significance. It is part of how you can make yourself memorable to others.

How do you feel about your names?

- *first name*

- *surname*

- *nicknames*

What particular meaning does your first name or family name have, such as its association with a town or other region?

How do you see yourself?

How else can you answer the question 'Who are you'?

It might be more important for you to say what you do for a living, how many children you have got, or what you like to do to relax. This response may be quite different from how you answered this question, say, five or ten years ago, and may also be different from how others see you.

This exercise will help you investigate your identity, as who you are affects what you do. It is in two stages, using the questionnaires in each stage.
Stage One: How you identify yourself
Stage Two: How this compares with the way others see you

Stage One: Your Identity   Fill in the questionnaire on the next page.

IDENTITY QUESTIONNAIRE – STAGE ONE

Imagine you are at a party. Someone asks you to tell them a bit about yourself. Think about what you would say. What is important for you to get across in this setting?

Rate the list below by putting a circle in the box on the scale of 1 to 5, 1 being 'very important' and 5 being 'not at all important', for the aspects of your identity listed.

Now draw a line between the first circle you drew and the second, and so on, until you have drawn a graph joining all the circles down the page. This is your 'party' identity line.

Now go back to the top of the list and repeat the questionnaire, putting crosses in the boxes, but this time imagine you are in a work situation and are again asked to say a bit about yourself. When you have finished, join up the crosses to form a 'work' identity line.

Compare the two lines for noticeable contrasts and similarities.

	Very important				Not at all important
	1	2	3	4	5
Your age					
Your job or profession					
Your ethnic origin					
Your gender; 'being a man'					
Your sexuality (straight, gay, bisexual, transsexual) . .					
Whether you have a life partner or not					
Where you come from					
What sports or teams you support					
What hobbies or interests you have					
Your family/children					
Your physical ability					
Your religion or spirituality					
Your political interest					

What other aspects of your identity, of who you are, are not covered in this list?

The differences between the two lines illustrate how your identity may vary in different settings.

Your answers to these questions may have changed as you've grown older and may continue to do so. You might like to predict which way your identity is currently going.

Aspects of your identity that you think will become LESS important in future:

Aspects of your identity that you think will become MORE important in future:

Stage Two:
How others see you

Once you have completed the questionnaire, ask one or two people you know and whose opinion you trust, such as your partner, a close friend or a work colleague, to fill in the same questionnaire (using the example on the following page) and give the answers for YOU. Ask them to fill it in giving the responses they think YOU would give. You can photocopy the questionnaire on the next page as many times as you want.

There are four main benefits of looking at the differences between other peoples' answers and your own:
- To see your 'blind spot'; something you can't see because you are too close to it
- The opinion of someone you trust can open your eyes and give you the opportunity to make some changes.
- To recognise aspects of yourself that you rate very highly and others do not.
- To identify a different way of seeing the world. This may be their blind spot and something you might not be able to change, but at least you will be aware of it and can constructively challenge it.

You can choose whether or not to do anything with this feedback.

IDENTITY QUESTIONNAIRE – STAGE TWO

Imagine the man who has given you this questionnaire is at a party. Someone asks him to tell them a bit about himself. Think about what he would say. What is important FOR HIM to get across in this setting?

Rate the list below by putting a circle in the box on the scale of 1 to 5, 1 being 'very important' to him and 5 being 'not at all important' to him, for the aspects of his identity listed.

Now draw a line between the first circle you drew and the second, and so on, until you have drawn a graph joining all the circles down the page. This is his 'party' identity line.

Now go back to the top of the list and repeat the questionnaire, putting crosses in the boxes, but this time imagine he is in a work situation and is again asked to say a bit about himself. When you have finished, join up the crosses to form a 'work' identity line.

Compare the two lines for noticeable contrasts and similarities. The differences between the two lines illustrate how his identity may vary in different settings.

	Very important				Not at all important
	1	2	3	4	5
His age					
His job or profession					
His ethnic origin					
His gender; 'being a man'					
His sexuality (straight, gay, bisexual, transsexual) . .					
Whether he has a life partner or not					
Where he comes from					
What sports or teams he supports					
What hobbies or interests he has					
His family/children					
His physical ability					
His religion or spirituality					
His political interest					

What other aspects of who he is are not covered in this list?

Thank you for your help

49

Comparing the questionnaires in Stage One and Stage Two: Were there any surprises? Any major differences between your own answers and theirs on your behalf?

These differences may be illuminating and you might want to consider how they have arisen.

For example, if you thought that your job or profession was important, and others thought it was less important for you, you may have learnt something important about how you come across at work.

Celebrating diversity and overcoming prejudice

In different situations people can become conscious of different aspects of their identity, depending on how others see them. For example, you might not be very aware of yourself as being a man, until you start a new job where many of your colleagues or your boss is a woman. Then this aspect of your identity may become more important to you. Other people may point it out, by how they act and what they say. This could be the case for someone you know who is from a different ethnic background, or if they are physically disabled, for example. People can be quick to 'judge a book by its cover' and relate to others only in terms of their physical appearance or ability, the few more obvious aspects of their identity.

The fact that 'Who are you?' is a simple question with complex issues will be the same for most people, irrespective of how they tend to be typecast. That is where stereotypes, such as racist or sexist ones, become harmful, because they only judge the cover and not the book.

How do you feel when someone only seems to see one aspect of your identity?

Being honest with yourself, are there any particular groups of people who you might tend to make generalisations about – for example because of an aspect of their identity, like their race or class?

This is what people are doing when they are prejudiced. Before they have found out more about you, they have already decided 'who you are' because of the way you speak or look or where you come from. You, like everyone else, deserve to be recognised for the whole person you are, and not just one or two aspects.

Your own equal opportunities policy

In so many aspects of life we are moving towards a more positive approach of valuing differences and diversity. Your own sex, sexuality, age, race, religion or faith, ability or disability will and does have an impact on all you meet. The degree of impact depends on the amount of prejudice you meet, and maybe also the judgements and assumptions you make also.

Yet all prejudices can be unlearned and overcome – and this is an opportunity for you to develop your own equal opportunities policy – to decide on and change how you are, how you behave and how you are treated by others.

There is now specific UK law covering sex, race, disability, sexual orientation and religion, and law on the way about age discrimination. Yet there are many other areas about each of our identities, which can cause others to be prejudiced against us or lead us to judge others.

This might be new for you to think about some of these areas, but as we move inevitably towards a more diverse world in every area, this is an opportunity for you to both contribute and receive more in your relationships at home, work or in your community – to gain from the richness which difference can bring.

You may want to set goals to explore more about groups of the population you know less about. This can help you find out more about yourself too.

51

Consider these questions about your own race, colour, gender, sexuality, spirituality/religion, age, level of disability or impairment, class etc.

- What do these mean to your life?
- How have they affected you?
- What doors have opened or closed as a result?
- How relevant are these to your future direction?
- How do you feel about people who are different to you in any of these respects?

If you find it hard to answer these questions, try to imagine how it would be if you were different in some respect to how you are. For example, if you are white, or able-bodied, spend some time imagining what your life would be like if you were black, or used a wheelchair.

> *The variety of our skin tones can confuse, bemuse, delight,*
> *Brown and pink and beige and purple, tan and blue and white.*
> *I've sailed upon the seven seas and stopped in every land,*
> *I've seen the wonders of the world, not yet one common man.*
>
> Maya Angelou

What do you celebrate about your own diversity?

Your attitudes

It is important to consider your attitudes as part of development, because they are crucial to your world view, and if the world is changing fast, your attitudes may also need to change and adapt in order to keep up. Inflexible attitudes could be the thing that would prevent you from recognising new opportunities.

Your attitudes are seen in many things including:

- What people around you prefer
- The way you feel about yourself – your own self-attitude
- Where you choose to live
- What you choose to do for a living

- Things you spend your money on
- The newspapers you read and the TV or films you watch
- The political preferences you have

Conditioned attitudes or 'head tapes'

As part of growing up everybody is conditioned to think in a certain way – to hold certain views about themselves and the world. Unquestioned attitudes that come from your upbringing tend to be the most rigidly held. This doesn't mean they are rigid attitudes in themselves.

- It may be that your parents or people who had a formative influence on you taught you to be open-minded.
- It may be that they have always said that foreign food is rubbish and you've always gone along with that without trying it for yourself!

But it is pretty certain that whatever they are, these attitudes will be quite hard for you to change, unless you want to.

It could be that your values have changed, and that certain old attitudes just don't fit you anymore. For example, you may now value information technology and will choose to ditch the old attitude that computers are only for 'experts'.

One way that conditioned attitudes will have a powerful influence on you is in the form of 'head tapes' – these are like tapes that keep playing in the back of your mind. They probably won't have come from you but from elsewhere: parents, the media, friends, school.

Here are some commonly heard head tapes:

'Work is never fun'
'Men are competitive'
'Women talk too much'
'Children are ungrateful'
'The way I speak is common'
'Finish what's on your plate'
'A real man drinks eight pints'
'Things always turn out badly for me'
'Mustn't grumble'
'Things aren't as good as in the old days'

Negative mind viruses

There is another way of describing these 'head tapes', particularly the negative ones that prevent you from making progress.

53

Professor Richard Dawkins proposes that attitudes and beliefs are like viruses such as the common cold – people catch them from each other and they spread through an organisation, a community or society as a whole, looking for the next person to play host for them.

For you the most important consequence of this might be that, where you live or work, in your department or team, there will almost certainly be certain negative beliefs that many people seem to agree on:

'We will be the first ones to get laid off when the cuts happen'
'There is no point in being good at your job because it will mean you are too valuable in your current job to be considered for promotion'
'Networking just means kissing the boots of people higher up in the organisation'

It is probably possible to provide evidence for these attitudes to be proved false just as easily as they can be proved true.

These negative beliefs may prevent you from taking responsibility for yourself and making progress, if you allow yourself to catch the same 'mental cold'.

There can also be positive mind viruses as well. These will spread in exactly the same way as negative ones, only their effort will be to enable you and the people around you to look for the very best opportunity in every situation.

Attitudes about yourself

Here are some positive mind viruses:

'Most people have lots of hidden talents'
'You can succeed if you try'
'You have a great future ahead of you'

Your attitude towards yourself develops out of your conditioning, your experience, and your free will too. This self-attitude is very important – in fact it is the key to your success.

Here are some examples of positive and negative attitudes which will greatly affect your self-confidence. Some of them are so powerful that they become self-fulfilling prophecies.

Negative	Positive
Where's the catch?	Where's the opportunity?
This will never work	I'll make this work
I've heard it all before	What else can I learn?
What's wrong here?	What's best about this?
I'm too old	I'm very experienced

Your attitude about yourself colours how other people see you.

If you have a positive attitude, you can bridge the gap between you and other people, making things happen that negative people don't have the energy to make work.

Optimistic people are given opportunities when cynical and inflexible people are passed over, which of course reinforces their negativity. So – keep the drive and energy that you have going. If you've lost it, take action to find it again.

It is a self-fulfilling prophecy: you are more likely to notice opportunities if you have a positive attitude and this is why positive people tend to achieve more.

Have you ever noticed if you buy something new, like a new piece of clothing, or even a car, suddenly you see other examples of it everywhere you go? This is because your eye has been 'tuned-in', to notice it. This is how positive attitudes work: they tune your thinking towards possibilities.

This is why it is vital that you consider how your attitudes have an impact on the world around you.

How do you know what your attitude is towards yourself? It may change, as with all your attitudes and opinions, depending on the company you keep, your mood, your level of motivation, or events.

Your self-attitude is the filter through which you see your life. You may not want everything rose-coloured, but you can only benefit from being more positive.

Superman or supermen?

If some of your unfulfilled values tend to be in the arena of 'the world'. This is not surprising as many people feel powerless to tackle single-handedly all the world's problems, such as crime, poverty, terrorism or global warming. Wouldn't it be nice to have cosmic powers to save the world? Unfortunately, there is no Superman.

But there are *supermen* and *women*. By being involved in this process, together with many other people, you are already helping on this world stage, by providing a more constructive mental atmosphere within which your generation and future ones can begin to make a difference. Even if you take small steps, yours combined with others will make for considerable change overall.

Self-awareness breeds creativity. Creativity breeds solutions.

This works on many levels: within yourself, within your family, for the organisations you spend time in and in the world as a whole.

Never doubt that a small group of committed citizens can change the world, indeed it is the only thing that ever has.

Margaret Mead – Social Anthropologist

Where do you want to go now?

Think about:

– adding to the notes section, where you can record any useful ideas in the blank pages at the end of the workbook
– deciding which chapter to go to next

Nasir – Leeds

Past

I was born into a poor ethnic background, controlled by my parents' strong Islamic beliefs. I grew up with these beliefs and wasn't strong enough to challenge them.

Present

I have now challenged these beliefs which has led to devastating consequences for my family. I have managed to pick up the pieces and have some semblance of a life.

Future

I hope to resolve the differences and heal wounds. I seek redemption.

4

The Journey

> " *Save your judgement of me until you have walked ten miles in my shoes* "
>
> Anon

Objective
- To review your journey so far, consider where you are now and explore possible options for your next steps

This chapter is important because
- You can capitalise on the huge resource of your life so far
- Being clearer about the different phases of your life will help you make decisions
- You can set fresh goals right now

Content
- Where have you been, and which way now?
- Your Life Map
- Where are you going?
- Your goal strategy

Where have you been, and which way now?

If you keep asking yourself key questions, you are likely to stay on course. You may be exactly where you want to be in your life, or you may be wondering how on earth you got here.

Most people have had many ups and downs but when you look at individuals' lives more closely, even so-called ordinary people have led extraordinary lives. However you got here, the journey may have been as exciting as a roller-coaster ride or as dull as driving down a one-way street.

Recognising the landscape you have travelled over and the key stopping places and events can be useful. You can:

- Identify the events that have given you energy
- See the key patterns of phases and how they might recur in future
- Stop repeating the unhelpful patterns
- Appreciate how surviving difficult times has made you strong
- Know where you earned your biggest achievements
- Realise that you have faced some event earlier or later than the average person
- Know what you don't want to do again
- Form ideas of how you would like to steer the next part of your life

Your Life Map

Being clear about your past brings more clarity to your future. In this practical exercise take yourself on an inner journey, using your imagination and memory. It is also a time for some healthy nostalgia. You are going to end up with a picture of your life so far. The prospect may be appealing or appalling to you. No one else has to see your picture – it is just a memory jogger for you personally.

Find a comfortable, private space where you can work undisturbed and feel 'at home'. Make sure you've got a good chunk of free time, at least an hour, to do it in.

This is for you to be clearer about your past, review it from where you are now rather than when you were in the throes of living it. Have some fun with it. Try not to think about what it will 'look like'. Let your memories and reflections emerge, in any order they come to you. It is your story, your road so far, so no one can judge it better than you.

Use the diagram on the next page, or if you want you can draw it on a larger sheet of paper.

It is meant to represent a picture of your life as a journey down this road. Imagine that you are looking along this road at the landscape of your life. Start with the nearest point of the road (at the bottom of the paper). This is your birth. The horizon can then represent your present, 'here and now', and the sky can be your future. This is just a suggestion and you can develop it however you like.

Work creatively and intuitively, allowing the map to 'make itself'. To help you, think about these particular aspects of life:

- Important people, family, relationships, mentors
- Important events – you can put in the dates
- Homes you have lived in
- Big changes – these could be on the bends of the road
- Good times and bad times
- Health issues (e.g. periods of hospitalisation or particular fitness for yourself or others close to you)
- Family and relationships
- World events that mattered to you (again the year may be helpful)

Work creatively, using words, drawings, pictures, even collages of things cut out from magazines or press cuttings. Try using lots of colour as this helps you enjoy it. Try also not to worry about whether it is 'pretty' – you can ignore the head tape (see page 53) that many people learnt at school about 'not being good at art'!

Remember this is not about making a 'work of art' – but it should be enjoyable.

Use the road and the landscape (or it could be the sea or even in space!) either side.

As an alternative option, you can use the 'lifeline' method following the example on page (see page 70). It is self-explanatory and works more in terms of thinking about life's ups and downs.

When you have finished this map, identify some phases which you have gone through, using the following input.

Life phases   Everybody's life goes through different phases and stages. Some are common to many people and some will be unique. By identifying the common ones, and putting a name to them, you can see how your life may pan out in future, more or less following the pattern set down by previous generations.

YOUR LIFE MAP

YOUR
FUTURE

NOW

YOUR
PAST

The following 'seven ages of man' are typical life phases that have been identified in many cultures, including that of Europe. The suggested ages are merely a guide and should not be regarded as 'cast in stone'. You can read them and then decide to what degree you fit in with this pattern. It is not better or worse if you have done so. It is just a guideline.

The important thing to notice about these life stages for yourself is that:

- The phases may well overlap, coincide or reverse their order
- Not everyone lives through all these phases
- Some men do them in a completely different order from the list
- Sometimes a phase is lived through more than once
- Some men live through phases which are not named here and have to find a name for these phases themselves

Phase one   **Birth** – a time of helplessness, being cared for – typical age: 0-7. This is a time when the care of other people, such as parents, guardians or teachers, will have had great influence on you. It is a time when you learnt to walk, talk, understand and make sense of the world. It is a time when you may have asked 'Why?', as in 'Why is the sky blue?' What do you know about this time in your life?

Phase two   **Childhood** – times of exploration – typical age: 7-14. This is the time when boys play without thinking much about the future. Friends can be important in this phase. It can be a carefree time, or a time of great distress if the will of adults is felt to have been overbearing. Think about how your world was for you as a boy. Was it good? Was there anything missing?

Phase three   **Manhood** – times of adolescence, initiation, puberty – typical age: 14-21. This is a time when you may have experimented with growing up. Usually growing up means some form of rebellion against the norms and values set by your parents or others bringing you up. You may have taken your first job, learnt to drive or done some travelling away from home. You may have been very influenced by what your friends thought and been very concerned about your abilities or looks. What did becoming a man mean to you?

Phase four   **Apprenticeship** – times of finding a role – typical age: 21-31. This is a phase of starting to 'settle down', deliberately deciding about a career, or falling into a particular job or profession because it seemed the obvious next step. It is the time when you may have found your feet in a particular role, either at work or in a family or group of friends. It can be a time when role models or mentors were an influence. Who were or are they for you?

Phase five

Partnership – times of finding life partner(s) – typical age: 20-35. This is the phase of serious relationships, perhaps the first time you lived with another person, got married or just settled into a long-term relationship. For some people it is a phase they may do later on in life, more than once, or never at all. For others it follows quite a predictable pattern. It can also be a time when a man becomes a father himself, either in or outside of a formal relationship. What does having a partner mean to you?

Phase six

Mid-life – the time of achievement and then questioning – typical age: 35-50. This is the time of major career development, fatherhood, major career changes. It can end with a 'mid-life crisis', a major questioning of values: 'What is life about?', 'Why am I doing this?', 'What is my real purpose?' These changes can come about from within, or be imposed from outside by changes in work or family life, such as unemployment, or separation/divorce.

Phase seven

Retirement – the time of new beginnings – typical age: 50 + As middle and old age approaches, what is being called the 'third age' can start. This can be a time of uncertainty, even a re-visiting of the helplessness of the birth phase or the playfulness of childhood. For some men it can be when life really starts; when dependent children or other relatives are no longer around and they can really do what they want to do, especially if they've planned ahead financially.

In this phase, inevitably, people are faced with thoughts of their own mortality. How do you want this phase to be? Death is a phase of life as well! How prepared do you want to be for it? Have you made a will? How do you want to be remembered or celebrated? What haven't you done yet in your life which you would regret not having done at the end of it all? This may seem morbid, but it might be really helpful to you, and to loved ones around you, if you sorted these things out.

If you look at your picture, you can begin to define the stages that you have been through, using the seven ages described above, in any order that is useful for you. You could invent *new* phases with *new* names that more accurately describe your own journey so far. Or you could use a combination of both your own and these phases.

⌐*Describe here the phases that you can identify in your own life map:*

⌐*What were the best and worst phases? Why?*

⌐*Describe any phases or experiences you are looking forward to, saying how you want them to be, ideally:*

Where are you going?

Having drawn your life map, you may be left with a:
- Feeling of great optimism – actually your life has been a lot more exciting than you've been giving yourself credit for
- Keenness to get on to the next steps
- Sadness or anger about past experiences
- Will to relate differently to the people around you now
- Hope for better things to come
- Certainty that you can achieve something now
- Sense of emptiness – that life hasn't been what it might have been and a need to fill it
- Feeling of satisfaction – 'I was pretty clear about myself and my life so far'
- Frustration – that drives you on to do things differently now

Now you can start to address the action you want to take for your future.

Keeping your options open

Before you start to make concrete plans, you can take good advantage of the review of your life's phases by bearing in mind the widest landscape of possibilities that are in front of you. You can keep your options completely open this way.

In a brainstorm, you list *all* the possibilities, without thinking about whether they are really feasible, or likely or not. Now is the chance to list all the things you might like to experience, all your hopes and dreams, without worrying about whether they are achievable aims or not. It is an opportunity to let your imagination fly. Some surprises may emerge along with the expected ones.

The list could include quite down to earth and practical options, such as:

- Get a job
- Go for promotion
- Learn to speak French
- Learn to use the computer properly
- Go paragliding
- Renovate my house
- Express my feelings more clearly
- Get married to my 'girlfriend'
- Have a civil partnership with my 'boyfriend'
- Move to another town
- Feel more confident in myself

And it can include the more fanciful, seemingly impossible options:

- Put my name down for the first public trip into space
- Become the head of a multinational corporation
- Stand for Parliament
- Have a family with ten children

List as many as you can here, and stop only when you can't think of any more.

Life is full of possibility. What do you really want? Which options can you really make happen? Keep this list in the spirit of keeping your options completely open. Who knows? One day you may fulfil even your most fanciful dream.

Vision and sense of direction

Now you can look ahead and see where the next turning point is, the brow of the next hill, or the next signpost. This will be the next point you are aiming for. It will mark a change that may happen:

- At work – e.g. a reorganisation of your department
- In your relationships – e.g. moving into a new house
- In the world of your community – e.g. new technology
- For yourself – e.g. learning a language

You may already be very clear about what you want to do (that may be why you're working with this workbook). But if you're not, consider two different approaches – being a person who has a vision, or a person who has a sense of direction.

Vision

Some people are natural visionaries. They often see things in their heads, and can actually describe the picture to others. Others may have a vision which drives them on of how life could be (of a social ill addressed, or a world based on different values). It is this vision which inspires and energises them, so they are motivated by achieving, in whatever measure, the vision that they have. Have a go at being a visionary. Imagine you are able to fast-forward a video of your life. See if you can see the picture in quite some detail: picture where you are, what you are doing and how you are feeling about it all.

You can choose to draw another picture of your future in the same way as you did for your past; or you can answer the following questions in relation to your work, your relationships, in your community or for yourself:

Where would you like to be or what would you like to be doing –

In a month's time?

In 6 months' time?

In a year's time?

In five years' time?

In ten years' time?

Think particularly about your feelings, about the pictures that come into your head or the words that you write. It is from your feelings that your motivation comes. When you are motivated you can then engage your will. If you don't regard yourself as much of a visionary then perhaps you operate from your sense of direction.

Sense of direction

People who operate from a sense of direction are motivated by a commitment to a way of doing things which takes them in a specific direction even if they cannot see the final goal. They are flexible and often spontaneously take up opportunities as they arise. They know how to make choices on a day-to-day basis and know that if they are prepared they will be ready to spot and grasp the opportunities when they arise.

People with a sense of direction are often extremely clear about where they don't want to go. If you consider yourself more of the direction type of person or are still not really clear about your future goals, then consider these questions to sharpen up your direction:

What do you get angry about?

What do you get really enthusiastic about?

If you were to die today, what would you regret not having done, achieved or experienced?

What ambitions do you have that remain unfulfilled? Think back to unrealised childhood ambitions.

What are your deepest-held values? Look back to page 44 and see which ones are not being met.

The dream/reality gap   Between the dreams of the future and the reality of the present there is often a gap. If the gap seems big and insurmountable then it puts people off trying. When you look at the gap you can:

- Find extra choices – particularly a third choice where you thought you only had two courses of action
- Look for the first steps, however small, that you can take in the right direction
- Challenge your own assumptions about the constraints that you place on yourself

Developing a flexible strategy to achieve your goals can help to close this gap.

> Take your dream seriously. You are here to become the best you
> can be. You owe it to yourself.
>
> Susan Hayward, *Begin It Now*

Your goal strategy

You can set whatever goals you want:

- Short-term and long-term
- Serious and more light-hearted
- Connected with work and connected with home
- Just for you and involving other people
- Outrageous and conventional
- Upfront and secret
- Within your current organisation and outside of it
- Within the familiar and into the unknown
- About doing more; or doing less and 'being' more

The next chapter will enable you to address your goals.

Where do you want to go now?

Think about:
- adding to the notes section, where you can record any useful ideas in the blank pages at the end of the workbook
- deciding which chapter to go to next

Huw – Hampshire

Past

My stable, comfortable, rather dull and uninspiring childhood kept me happy until I started to explore – then the illusion was shattered. I explored in the playground of wild ideas and hidden fruits with some abandon and little practicality, which rolls into my life now with a sense of joy at being different; different from others and different from who I was yesterday.

Present

I have written my own happiness and serenity in creating a stable and comfortable house which nurtures me like a nest, from which I now fly. My best qualities are summed up by the English words wit, curiosity and vision, and the French 'joie de vivre', whilst my worst qualities are impatience, fear, inertia and a tendency to write long convoluted sentences.

Future

I will be living in a contented, rural idyllic nest from which I will fly into the challenging and creative world of project development, in

the beautiful parts of Europe and possibly beyond (why not?). I would like to be remembered as a loving, unique and responsible husband, father, uncle and grandfather, as a happy, successful and charismatic man who made a difference.

Norman Neal

The Lifeline
(see diagram on next page).

Norman Neal – The Lifeline

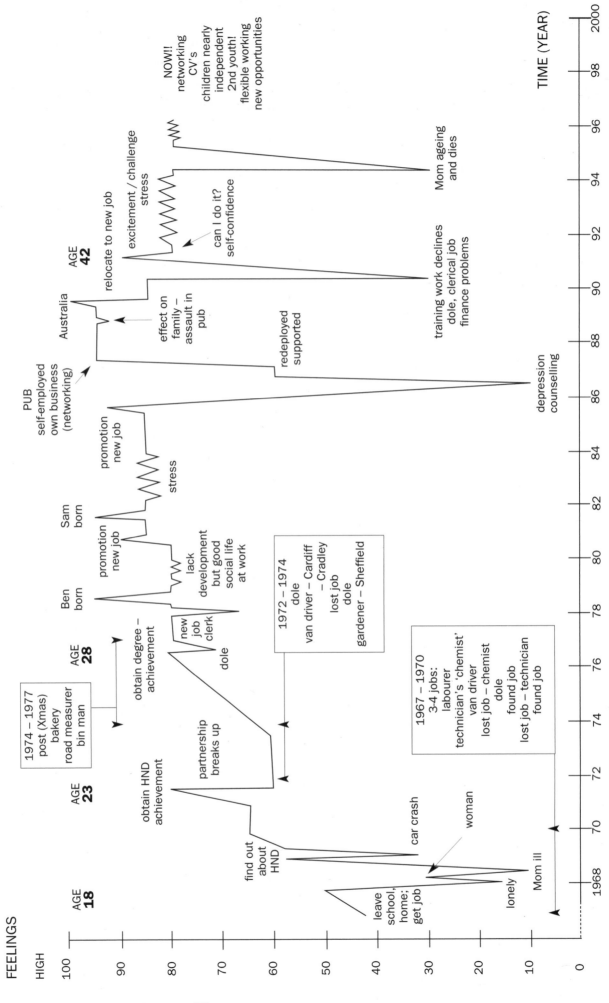

70

Setting Goals

> **"** *Men live by positive goals, individual and collective, a vast variety of them, seldom predictable, sometimes incompatible* **"**
>
> Sir Isaiah Berlin

Objective
To develop a goal strategy that provides steps for action which are:
- **S**pecific
- **M**easurable
- **A**chievable
- **R**ealistic
- **T**ime-bound

This chapter is important because
- In order for *Navigator* to be worthwhile you need goals that you can achieve, and be able to take clear steps towards them
- This chapter focuses on your goal strategy

You can complete the 'goal strategy' in this section as you go on, adding more to it as you progress through *Navigator*.

Content
- World goals
- Your goal strategy
- Picture your goals
- Your strategy document

World goals

Before you start to construct this strategy document for yourself, pause for a moment and consider what positive goals you might have for the world, for the whole of humanity. This might seem a tall order – very often you may find yourself feeling apathetic or powerless when it comes to this bigger picture. Most people do. The 'world stage' is a big place – most people don't feel they can do much about it.

But a vision is a very powerful thing, especially if it is shared by lots of people. So you are entitled to ask yourself: **'What sort of a world do I really want?'**

If you have a vision of that, and hold it in your mind's eye, you can imagine the power of this vision if it is shared by many people. It is this sort of vision that can change the world. And you have the power to do it.

What sort of world do you really want? What 'world vision' do you have for the future?

For example, a world of:

- Harmony
- Wealth
- Quiet, friendly neighbourhoods
- Technology
- Simplicity
- Education for all
- Pollution-free cities
- Electric cars
- Widely-travelled people

A world vision is often achieved through the day-to-day actions of many millions of people. If people have harmonious relationships, for example, that will add up to a more harmonious world.

Name one practical thing you can do which would contribute to a world change:
For example: recycle my bottles, improve my relationships with colleagues

You can always add such 'world goals' to your own goal strategy, or recognise how some of your goals, if multiplied many times, would add up to a better world. You may have more 'world power' than you thought.

Your goal strategy

Why have goals?

Goals can:

- Help you express yourself
- Fulfil your values
- Motivate you to keep going
- Be the 'wind in your sails'

If you don't have any:

- You may drift
- You may put up with second best
- The world will pass you by
- Things change without your consent
- You may be forced to make changes anyway

Goals can be:

- Big or small
- Trivial or very important
- Short-term or long-term
- For any aspect of your life:
    - work
    - home
    - skills
    - inner or outer
    - relationships
    - for the world in general
    - for yourself specifically
- 'Being' goals – about doing less and relaxing more
- 'Doing' goals – about getting your act together

Goals can change and grow. They can start out in one direction and completely change course.

That means goals can be flexible, as well as leading to specific action. If you have goals and you don't achieve them, you may feel disappointed and de-motivated. Consider your track record – have you a 'history' of goals that you have tried and have not worked

73

out? For example, you may have tried to give up smoking or lose some weight, and it hasn't worked out, so you don't bother trying again.

What is your track record with setting goals? How successful have you been at setting and achieving goals?

Four things to consider when embarking on your goals strategy, to make sure it works:

Vision
— Where do I want to go?
— What are the opportunities around me?

Flexibility
— How can I adjust my vision as I go?
— How well do I understand others' needs?

Will
— Do I really want this, enough to persist, to push through?

Small steps
— What is the first practical step?

'SMART'
Actions towards goals benefit from being 'SMART' which stands for:
— **S**pecific
— **M**easurable
— **A**chievable
— **R**ealistic
— **T**ime-bound

This ensures that things do happen and don't drift.

This formula will give you action points for your goals, so that you can take the first step on a journey towards your goal. Take a step at a time, and you can walk a thousand miles.

Picture your goals

You have a creative, intuitive, visionary side, as well as a rational and down-to-earth aspect in your thinking.

When you approach such an important topic as your goals, it may be useful to explore both the vision as well as the concrete practicalities. This will help you cover all your options, and make sure your goals are as wide-ranging as possible. Working creatively can also be fun!

Approach your goals in a visionary way as well as working on your strategy. A simple way to do this is to draw a picture of your own goals.

The next page has been left blank, except for a circle in the middle in which 'my goals' is written. If this isn't enough space for you, take a big sheet of paper and use this instead.

Link all your goals out from the centre circle, as if you were drawing a road or rail route map.

Try to:

- Use pictures as well as words
- Use lots of different colours
- If a goal seems important, make it larger
- If a goal seems less important, make it smaller
- Start from the centre and work outwards, putting in your most important goals first, as they occur to you.
- Make links between your goals
- Draw in the consequences, for yourself and others, of these goals; and
- Draw out action points at the very edge of the page

Don't censor it or worry about whether your goals are possible at this stage. Now is the time to be as outlandish and crazy as possible. You can refine this into 'sensible' action later.

MY GOALS

Your strategy document

The rest of this chapter can be added to at any time. As you progress on your navigation, you can make new links to old goals or create new goals, depending on what occurs to you.

This strategy consists of six blank pages of six columns. When you get to the last blank page, photocopy it before you fill it in, so you have plenty of sheets available which you can add.

Your goal strategy can keep on growing and changing, throughout your life.

Column one – your goals

In this column you write your overall goals.
- You can be as general as you like at this stage
- You can put more than one goal in this column
- If you feel it is an important goal, leave a bit more space between it and the next one

Column two – explanatory notes

In this column, add any extra information that is relevant to this goal. It may link this goal to:
- A chapter, topic or some learning you have covered in the workbook or in the *Navigator* programme that you feel may be relevant. (For example, if you feel that you will need to be assertive to achieve this goal, write in the relevant learning from Chapter 13, where you look at assertiveness.)
- Another goal
- Something you discovered in your goal vision picture
- Any blocks, previous history or things to watch out for
- Anything else that you think is relevant to this goal

As with the whole document, you may need to come back to this column as you progress – you don't have to fill it all in at once.

Column three – possible action

In this column you list all the possible things you could do towards this goal.
For example:
- What skill do you need? Qualifications? And the steps to getting them?
- How much money is needed?
- What motivation and determination do you need?
- What contacts and support do you need?
- How you will need to change your attitude, your image, your visibility?
- What will you have to give up?
- What information will you need?

**Column four
– consequences for
self and others**

If you achieve a goal, things will change in your life. These changes will have some consequences. These consequences may be good as well as challenging. Other people may choose to react or may feel something as a consequence of your goal. If you don't consider this, these consequences may become a block.

Consider all the possible consequences, particularly for those close to you.

For example, how will others react if you become more assertive? How will that affect what you do?

**Column five
– action chosen**

Now is the time to choose from the possible actions what you will do.

These chosen action points must be:

S – Specific – what action will you take? For instance, 'Be more assertive' is a good intention, but vague. 'I will listen more at the next team meeting on Tuesday' is more like it!

M – Measurable – how will you know if you have achieved this goal? What will be the measure of success? For instance, 'I will ask a trusted colleague if they felt I listened well.'

A – Achievable – can it really be done? How do you know?

R – Relevant – does it relate to one of your values, something that really matters to you, or is it just a good intention, like a New Year's resolution that you break on 2 January.

T – this is the Time frame – which goes in column 6 below: 'By when?'

You may feel there is a gap between what you'd like and the reality. If the gap is very big, it may put you off from trying to change anything. But you have a lot of choices to make here, even if they are not all easy ones. Your development is all about:

- Finding the choices where there appears to be no choice
- Looking for the first simple steps to take you in the right direction
- Challenging your assumptions about the constraints you feel

Make sure it is a practical, small step in the right direction!

**Column six
– by when?**

Give yourself a time-frame, and maybe tell your coach or supporter about it so they can check whether you have achieved it.

A time-frame will ensure your action does not 'drift'. Make sure it is a realistic time frame. For instance, 'I will redecorate the whole house by a week on Tuesday' is probably not a realistic time-frame, whereas 'I will start with the spare bedroom, and buy the paint at the weekend' is 'smart' action with a realistic time-frame.

Remember: You will keep returning to, and refining, this goal strategy. Don't worry if it seems a little bare at first. You have the rest of your life to achieve your goals. All you need to start with is a 'smart' move.

Goals aren't set in concrete – they can change. Your goal strategy pages are very much a working document.

YOUR GOAL STRATEGY

YOUR GOAL	EXPLANATORY NOTES	POSSIBLE ACTION	CONSEQUENCES FOR SELF AND OTHERS	ACTION CHOSEN	BY WHEN?

YOUR GOAL STRATEGY

YOUR GOAL	EXPLANATORY NOTES	POSSIBLE ACTION	CONSEQUENCES FOR SELF AND OTHERS	ACTION CHOSEN	BY WHEN?

YOUR GOAL STRATEGY

YOUR GOAL	EXPLANATORY NOTES	POSSIBLE ACTION	CONSEQUENCES FOR SELF AND OTHERS	ACTION CHOSEN	BY WHEN?

YOUR GOAL STRATEGY

YOUR GOAL	EXPLANATORY NOTES	POSSIBLE ACTION	CONSEQUENCES FOR SELF AND OTHERS	ACTION CHOSEN	BY WHEN?

YOUR GOAL STRATEGY

YOUR GOAL	EXPLANATORY NOTES	POSSIBLE ACTION	CONSEQUENCES FOR SELF AND OTHERS	ACTION CHOSEN	BY WHEN?

YOUR GOAL STRATEGY

YOUR GOAL	EXPLANATORY NOTES	POSSIBLE ACTION	CONSEQUENCES FOR SELF AND OTHERS	ACTION CHOSEN	BY WHEN?

You have a choice

The only magic of personal development is how common sense, hard work, some vision and the small practical steps towards it can achieve fantastic results. All of this is born out by the experience of many people who have navigated such a journey through life.

But to make it work you have to really want to do it, and continue to want to do it.

You have a choice – every day

Every day you can decide whether to make an effort, take a measured risk, a further step and so on.

You may decide to halt for a while – you have that choice too, every day.

You can always start again. It's up to you.

You have total freedom in your choice

No one is going to make it happen for you. That means no one can make you do it.

What you do, and how you do it, are entirely your business.

Men can feel immense pressure to go out and 'achieve' – that is great if that is what you want to do. In that case we say 'DO IT!'

If not – if you want to put your energy into other things, and relax a bit more, spend more time with your family, or be by yourself, we can say 'BE IT!'

It can either be:
    'Don't just sit there, do something!'

Or equally:
    'Don't just do something, sit there!'

Most of us are looking for a balance between these two. Whatever it is you choose to do, we wish you the best success, however it is you choose to define it.

Where do you want to go now?

Think about:
– adding to the notes section, where you can record any useful ideas in the blank pages at the end of the workbook
– deciding which chapter to go to next

John Lewis – Crossing the divide from manual work to management

On leaving school I had no idea which career direction I was heading in. My parents guided me into an engineering workshop, where I lasted about 9 months before I became bored and felt closed in. I then tried working on a building site in a variety of trades, from labourer to carpenter. I soon found that I enjoyed this environment. Fortunately the site foreman saw I had a flair for woodwork and put me forward to do an apprenticeship in carpentry and joinery. When working on site I found that all the various trades help each other, so whenever I was asked to assist with another trade I never refused, which has paid off in my later life as I have a good understanding concerning all the major trades within the construction industry.

Unfortunately my marriage then failed, and what followed was a time when I was at the lowest I have ever felt in my life. But I soon found out that the world does not stop because I had problems. I had bought my ex-wife out of the house and my mortgage was now astronomical. I grew up and very quickly. I sat down to take stock, of what I wanted out of life, where I was going and what I wanted to achieve. I set out a plan of action for the way forward, with a strategy towards the two main goals I had:

1 *To keep my house, and in order to do that:*
2 *To attain promotion to the position of foreman.*

By working harder (and smarter) than ever before, I became foreman. I then set myself another goal of becoming the Area Supervisor which was two further steps up the promotional ladder. On my first attempt I did not achieve the position of Area Supervisor but I was made Assistant Area Supervisor. I was disappointed about this – I genuinely thought I was the best man for the job, like we all feel when we don't get the promotion we want.

At about this time, I got to know the woman who was in charge of the Construction Division where I was working. I found this working relationship uplifting and admired her all the more for the challenge she must have faced as a woman in that role.

When a senior managerial position became vacant that had nothing to do with the Construction Division, I was asked if I would step in and carry out the duties of this post for approximately 6 months on a secondment. This position meant that I worked directly with the Directorate of the local authority. I felt I had risen

to this challenge effectively, not having any working experience of most of this department's key activities. However, when the position was appointed formally, I was unsuccessful with my application. I would be lying if I said that I was not disappointed. I have looked back at my interview and saw that there were points which I could have improved on but that will be for next time.

I believe I am the only person who knows what I want, and my motto has always been: 'work for it'.

6

Getting Support

> " *Trust begets trust; fear escalates fear* "
>
> Jack Gibb – *Trust*

Objective	• To get clear about who helps and hinders you on your journey
This chapter is important because	• You are not alone • It helps you identify where you can get the best support for the changes you will face • More opportunities will arise for you if you have a wider network
Content	• Getting support • Coaching – useful information • Taking risks • Your support network

Getting support

Generally, people cope better with changes when they have some help and support – some fellow travellers on their journey. You can get support from a very wide range of people:

- Your partner
- Your family
- Your friends
- Your work colleagues
- Professional agencies
- People you meet on the off-chance

Support can come in lots of different forms. Sometimes it is in the form of specific advice. More often it is just another person knowing you, accepting how you are, understanding how you 'tick' and just 'being there'. You don't need to be in difficulty to benefit from it – it is useful at any time.

Coaching – useful information

No doubt you've had times in your life when you have had a 'jolly good talking to'. Now is a chance to make sure you get a jolly good listening to.

Choose a friend or colleague, perhaps someone else on the *Navigator* programme to act as your coach in your development. You can do the same in return for them. Make sure it is someone you feel will listen to you.

The point of having a coach is that:

- You gain extra information
- You get the opportunity to test out and confirm your view or ideas
- You can gain feedback about parts of yourself or your ideas that you may not be able to see clearly yourself
- You may find a good reason to rethink your ideas or strategy
- Someone else may have the contacts that you need to make your ideas a success
- You can benefit from giving as well as receiving

Some guidelines for you to agree between you and your coaching partner:

- Confidentiality – you can tell others what you did but not what either of you said
- Divide the time in half and take it in turns to talk while the other listens without making judgements – be strict so both of you get time

- Find a private, quiet space
- Make it a regular occasion – once every week, two weeks or month but not too spread out
- Use a session to address a particular question, rather than just as a rambling chat
- If you can't make it for some reason, make another date, then and there
- Be prepared to find another person if the first attempt didn't quite work out; or have more than one coaching partner if you want.

A coaching partner is simply someone who will listen, give you comments on ideas and know that you will follow them *only if you think they are right for you.* A coaching partner leaves you free to make your own mind up about what you do about any advice.

You may find different people better at supporting you and listening to you with different subjects. Remember:

- You may feel uncomfortable at first but it can become really valuable if you persist
- Asking for coaching can be a sign of strength
- Coaches form part of a support network that is vital for your future
- Being a coaching partner for someone else can be a rewarding process for you and an increasingly desirable skill in the workplace

Coaching works when there is a good balance of support and challenge in the relationship.

Support – might be about giving people encouragement, positive feedback, celebrating their achievements and building them up.

Challenge – might mean reminding them of something they said they want to do that they have been avoiding, or raising their awareness about something in their behaviour they hadn't spotted.

These need to be handled respectfully, carefully and considerately, with a mind to assertiveness (see chapter 13).

Too much support without challenge might become a bit too cosy and comfortable. This is OK for a friendship but may not be developmental enough to be called 'coaching'. On the other hand too much challenge without the support may be uncomfortable and make people defensive.

There needs to be a good balance which you can discuss and agree as you go.

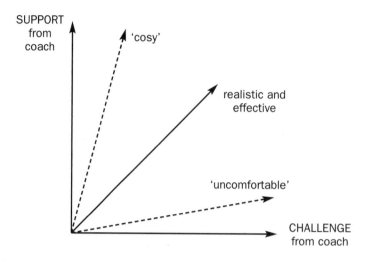

Getting support matters because:

- It gives you more choice
- Giving support makes you invaluable and important to other people, and makes you memorable
- You don't have to do everything on your own
- You might get things done better or faster with the help and support of others
- With the right support, change can become an opportunity rather than a disaster.

When my father was made unemployed, he was devastated. He didn't know what to do. Even though he had hated his job, he was lost. Then my mother called a family conference, and we discussed what else he was good at. He was amazed when we told him about his talents! He loved photography and video, so we encouraged him in that direction. With his redundancy money, he set himself up with a small wedding photography and video business. He didn't earn masses out of it, but five years later he could retire, when he was ready to.

John

Getting good support involves taking a risk, but the benefits can be clear as in the example above. Risk and trust are closely related in a two-way process. If you take risks with people and show that you are trustworthy, they will generally be more open with you.

Taking risks   If you don't take risks, you are limiting your possibilities. If you want to learn anything new or change something for the better for yourself, you will inevitably have to take a risk.

> *If you always do what you've always done,*
> *Then you'll always get what you've always got.*

For example, how will people know that you need their support? You will have to ask them for it. They probably won't offer what you need spontaneously. You will therefore have to risk rejection. But risks do not have to be 'all or nothing' – they can be measured, and you can control how much of a risk you take. This is true for risks of all types.

Looking at the following:

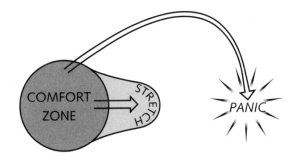

| too quiet/comfy | bit of stretch | too much! |
| ⇒ no learning | ⇒ learning! | ⇒ no learning |

Comfort zone   In this zone, you carry on exactly as you are. You don't learn anything new. You are comfortable. This can feel like a bit of a rut – it may be 'velvet-lined' and cosy, but life may not be stimulating. For example there are opportunities for promotion but you choose to stay where you are. Not much learning here.

Panic zone   In this zone, huge risks are taken. If you have a fear of heights, this would be the zone in which you decide to combat your fear with a bungy-jump! Or perhaps in work you go from being a junior clerical officer straight to being head of department. This may give you lots of sleepless nights and you may not perform very well at all. The risks are too great and the shock too overwhelming. Not much learning here either.

Stretch zone   In this zone, you are stretched beyond your comfort zone without taking such a big risk that you feel unsupported or too 'out on a limb'. It is a measured risk, taken in stages. Perhaps you go for a small promotion which would stretch you, but not too much. Here's where the learning is.

It is important to remember:

- Small measured stretches usually have more lasting results than a giant leap
- Your stretch zone is unique to you – what is a big risk for you may not be for someone else and vice versa. You are the judge for your stretches.
- People may respond bravely by stretching with you
- People may respond fearfully by resisting your stretch

What would be a measured risk for you?

At work (e.g. talking to my manager about promotion)

In relationships (e.g. telling my partner when I feel upset)

For yourself (e.g. learning to swim)

In the world/community (e.g. talking to my new neighbour)

What other measured risks can you take?

Your support network

You do not need to carry on the same way for ever and ever, ending up wondering why you feel isolated and out on a limb. For some men this realisation is a bolt from the blue.

Who in your life helps you, who hinders you and who is there that can help you?

Your support network is not just a nice thing to have – it is an important tool for your effectiveness and satisfaction.

In exploring support, you can look at:
- Important positive influences on your life
- Helps and hindrances
- Networking formally and informally

Your Influence Map

People have had an influence on your life, and vice versa. Some of these will have been more supportive than others. In this exercise, you will explore the main influences on your life, as you see it now.

People around you have:
- Encouraged you or held you back
- Influenced your thinking, feelings, attitudes
- Given you courage and inspiration
- Received support or been influenced by you
- Been a constant influence, positively or negatively

For example:

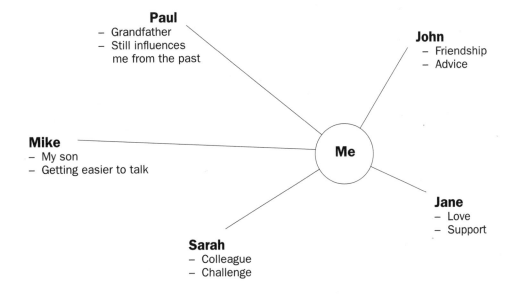

Paul
– Grandfather
– Still influences me from the past

John
– Friendship
– Advice

Mike
– My son
– Getting easier to talk

Me

Jane
– Love
– Support

Sarah
– Colleague
– Challenge

Write your name in the circle in the Influence Map. Around this circle, draw in your map. You can play with how you do it, altering the size of the names or their distances from you to represent the different influences. You can also use different colours for the different types of support and influence.

INFLUENCE MAP

Help and hindrance   Reviewing this map:

Where have the positive and conscious sources of help and support come from?

What additional sources of help and support do you want to build up?

How have you been a source of support and influence for others?

Keyholders   Many men seem to have experienced a time when one other person had a particular formative influence on them. It may not have been for very long, and may not even have been someone they knew very well. Often it is just that they were in the right place at the right time and did or said the right thing that prompted an important change. These people act as keyholders for others. Their role is to offer a key to a new phase in your life.

Andrew was a young man working in a council department when his senior departmental director, who was just about to retire, told him out of the blue that he thought he should apply for a particular further education course relevant to his work. Although he didn't know his senior manager that well, Andrew did so, and once he had completed the course, this led quickly to new doors and promotion opening up for him.

Watch out for your keyholders. It may be that they will arrive in the form of a chance remark, or it may be that someone acts as a constant source of support and ideas.

You can be the keyholder for others too. It can be a very rewarding role to play.

97

⌐ *Which keyholders can you think of in your life? How have they helped?*

⌐ *What particular help do you need from a keyholder right now?*

⌐ *For whom have you acted as a keyholder, and how?*

⌐ *Who can you become a keyholder for?*

Don't underestimate what you have to offer others.

Active goodwill   If you think of everybody you know (and research shows that this will be about 500 people), they are likely to fall roughly into three categories along a scale of helpfulness:

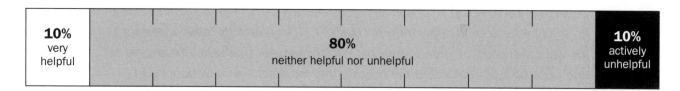

10% very helpful	80% neither helpful nor unhelpful	10% actively unhelpful

- 10% are people who will actively help you – no matter what
- 80% are people who aren't particularly interested in you, but would help, if you took the initiative with them
- 10% are people who don't like you, or what you stand for, and will actively hold you back given the chance

The 10% of active supporters – they are already 'on your team', as you probably are on theirs. Keep in touch with them, as these relationships need some maintenance! The 10% who are actively unhelpful are not worth worrying about. It is a waste of your time and energy trying to change their minds, and you can't expect to win everyone over.

The great majority of people you know will be in the 80% in the middle. Here is where you can make a difference. They can be described as having 'latent goodwill' towards you. They probably couldn't care less about you at present! This is where you can turn their latent goodwill into active goodwill. You have to take the initiative here.

⌐ *Who do you know in the 80% group that you might try to move into your support network?*

⌐ *What might they offer you?*

⌐ *What might you be able to give in return?*

Networking
Networking can benefit everybody. Networking can mean many things, from building an active social life to communication by computers. Here 'networking' is building a positive and varied group of mutual support.

For some people, networking is a jargon word, used by people who spend their time feathering their own nest. They might see networking as 'crawling', an activity undertaken by smooth operators who just want to benefit themselves.

But there is a clear difference between good networking and more selfish crawling or ego-centric behaviour:

Networking	Crawling
• Works up and down the organisation, where you make yourself known to people in a wide and diverse variety of roles	• Only works up the organisation, where you make yourself known only to those in powerful positions
• Can be for you and for others; you can put other people in touch with one another for their benefit	• Is only for you, where you actively put others down for your own benefit and in order to build yourself up
• Being yourself and forming genuine working relationships and friendships with people	• Pretending to be something you're not and having acquaintances who don't really know you
• Because you want to	• Because you feel you have to
• People respect you for being yourself	• People disrespect you for being selfish

Networking can be a very important activity, not just for your own development but also for the development of others and for your organisation or community.

Your own network

Your own network is made up of everyone you know. If you extend that to everyone they know, you can imagine a vast matrix of supportive relationships. In the film, 'Six Degrees of Separation',[1] a story unfolds based on the idea that everyone in the world is connected to everyone else by a thread of only six relationships, as the title suggests. That may be stretching the idea quite far, but it does give a sense of how interconnected we human beings are as a species.

Your network of contacts may offer the best chance you have of finding a job. The Chartered Institute of Personnel and Development highlighted personal contacts as a better source of vacancies than an employment agency.

You are connected to a very wide range of people:

- Family
- Neighbours
- Through your children
- Through mutual friends
- Through a spiritual or religious community
- Through your school or college
- Supporting the same sports team
- Hobby or interest groups
- People you meet on holiday

- Through your workplace
- Fellow commuters
- Fellow professionals
- People in other organisations
- People from the same town or area
- People you meet on courses
- People with similar interests worldwide

There are clear benefits in having as wide a network as possible. It gives you greater flexibility to achieve your goals, and greater adaptability to change or just the chance to be at ease with yourself and the world. You don't have to like everyone you know – they may just give you another perspective on life.

How widespread are your contacts across the categories?

Are there enough people outside work?

At work, are they spread around many departments or just from your own?

When do you meet people who are totally different from you?

What do you do to keep in contact with people?

What could you do to network more?

Which people do you need to/want to make contact with?

Formal networks   There are also formal networks specifically for men. In Appendix 1 you will find some addresses of organisations that exist specifically for the support of men's issues. Men's groups have been around for a long time and are a very effective support mechanism for a growing number of men. They can be formal and goal-orientated, such as a single fathers support group, or informal forums for discussion, sharing or thoughts, experiences, creativity and feelings, or just an opportunity to meet men from diverse backgrounds and relax in their company.

There are a whole range of specific approaches to men's issues, but most men's groups are made up of ordinary men who live in the same area and value the special support men can give each other, coming from all backgrounds, races, sexual orientations, ages and experiences.

What would be the advantages for you in joining a men's group?

How might a men's group be different from existing get-togethers, such as going to the pub?

Where do you want to go now?

Think about:
– adding to the notes section, where you can record any useful ideas in the blank pages at the end of the workbook
– deciding which chapter to go to next

Tim – Gloucestershire

Past

My early life was like being chained to a set of expectations and roles, covertly and overtly imposed, which, until the release came, led me to strive for perfection and recognition for being male.

Present

Through enlightenment and increased personal awareness, I feel that I am free of the chains, and can travel to new-found freedom.

Future

My vision is being free from all these traditional expectations and discovering my whole self and being myself. Discovering new and long-lasting friendships with loving and supportive people, especially men, will give me the opportunity to share, listen, discover, learn and have fun with free people.

Geoff Mead

'A path with heart'

I first got involved in personal development about 20 years ago when, whilst working as a chief superintendent in the police force, I became fascinated by interpersonal communication and relationships. Courses on facilitation, mentoring and consultancy opened up a new and sometimes confusing world of feelings. I felt that I had previously been living my life in two dimensions, in black and white.

Perhaps precipitated by this awareness, a crisis in my marriage led me into relationship counselling and then individual Gestalt therapy. Later I attended some events for men and joined a year-long men's group which met for a total of about twenty days in 'wilderness' locations, far removed from everyday life. I am currently a member of another men's group. This time it is self-organising and comprises about eight men, all in our forties and early fifties.

These experiences have been influential for me in a number of ways:
– *To find a solid sense of my masculinity that is grounded in my own life and values, not from popular macho culture.*
– *To gain a new outlook on work and life based on what I truly*

want for myself, not based on the desire for others' approval. This is hugely empowering.

- *I now relate differently to other men: more open, loving and accepting of who they are, less competitive and fearful. This includes developing a real friendship with another man for the first time in my life.*

- *I am less confused in my dealings with women – better able to distinguish between friendship, love, intimacy and sex, and less reliant on women for emotional and physical support.*

- *I now recognise and honour my own creativity, in painting, poetry, prose and dance. We are all creative beings, I believe – all it takes is a little faith and courage. My living space is decorated with my own pictures and objects.*

- *I am living a life with more integrity and authenticity. I am developing a sense of who I am in the world, and accepting my unconditional right to be. This leads to trouble sometimes with others, such as my wife and family.*

- *I am opening myself more to the universe, and I am beginning to make contact with my own spiritual nature. This is a source of wonder and puzzlement as I seek a form of practice in which to enact and explore this side of my life.*

I am sure there are many other ways in which my involvement with personal development and Menswork have affected me. I feel I am on a never-ending journey through my own life. I do what I must to survive and thrive. I feel that I walk with a stumbling gait, making mistakes and experimenting, learning how to walk a 'path with heart' and not settle for the 'famished road'.

Work in Place

> **"** *Work is love made visible.* **"**
>
> Kahlil Gibran, *The Prophet*

> **"** *There is no such thing as a career path. It is crazy paving*
> *And you have to lay it yourself.* **"**
>
> Dominic Cadbury,
> Chairman of Cadbury-Schweppes

Objectives
- To find out what you want out of your work
- To alert you to organisations and how power works within them

This chapter is important because
- You spend about a third of your life at work, if you're employed
- You may find there are pressures on you to work or earn
- Most people have questions about work
- Even if you aren't planning any changes yourself, the world of work is changing fast around you
- You can enjoy your work, whatever it is

Content
- What is work for you?
- Picture your career
- Striking your balance
- Different ways to work
- You and your organisation
- Gaining recognition
- Your personal power

What is work for you?

In this chapter you explore work in its widest sense – a paid or voluntary job, self-employment, looking for work, 'working' in the family home, choosing not to work in the conventional sense.

Other work options include:

- Part-time work
- Job sharing
- Voluntary reduced work time
- Flexitime
- Parental leave and paternity leave
- Term-time working only for parents
- Employment breaks
- Sabbatical leave
- Self-employment and contract working
- Working from home
- Project working in different areas

If work to you means paid employment, then it is something that you may spend a lot of your life doing. A forty to fifty-hour week means that you will spend approximately 40% of your whole waking life doing work, or travelling to and from it. This is a lot of our energy and time. Therefore, you deserve to get the most out of it you can.

- *Overall, 67 per cent of women and 79 per cent of men aged 16-64 are in employment*
- *People aged 25-44 have the highest employment rates: 73 per cent for women and 88 per cent for men.*
- *Only 9 per cent of male employees work part-time, compared with 43 per cent of female employees. The largest group of male part-time employees is aged under 25.*

Equal Opportunities Commission (2003 figures)

The issue of work raises some big questions. Some of them are:

- What is work for?
- What sort of work have other men in your family done? It may be that you have followed in the family footsteps or have broken out in a totally new direction.
- Do you live to work, or work to live?
- If you have children, or plan to, what sort of work do you picture them having?

- How much of what you do is 'men's work', or does that distinction between men's work and women's work no longer apply?
- How much of the housework do you get involved in?

These are all questions that relate to your own work career in the wider scheme of things, as part of the generations before you and after you. Very often, the influences of those before and after you can be quite powerful in setting your own horizons.

A significant number of UK fathers regard their jobs as 'just a means of earning a living'. Yet everything from bringing up a family and looking after a home to organising a leisure activity will involve some form of 'work'. It may not feel like work, but it will involve a lot of your effort, time and energy.

As the world of work changes, with more part-time, job-sharing, self-employment etc. work will increasingly mean different things to people. So it is important to think about how you define it for yourself, in the widest sense.

So what does your work mean to you?
For instance: It's just paid employment.
Everything is work – work just means everything you 'have to do'.

Getting what you want from work

Whether you are happy where you are or have a burning desire to move on, in this day and age you will benefit from having some sense of what you want to get out of your work.

If you find yourself more on the 'live to work' than 'work to live' end of the scale, then there are important questions you might have about your identity and values. Work for you becomes more of your whole reason for living, and therefore it is vital for you to feel satisfied with what you do as a career.

If you find yourself more on the 'work to live' end of the spectrum, then the questions are about getting exactly what you need from your job, in order to do the other things that are important to you.

107

What do you want from work? Rank these factors in order of importance 1-16:

☐ Income

☐ Pension

☐ Security

☐ Satisfaction

☐ Fulfilment

☐ Easy journeys

☐ Keeping busy

☐ Professional achievement

☐ Just 'having a job'

☐ Friendship, comradeship

☐ Prospects for promotion

☐ Self-development, new skills, new opportunities

☐ Changing or affecting the world for the better

☐ Being part of something

☐ Other – add your own

☐ Inspiration

How many of your highest ranking ones are being met?

What might you now add to your goal strategy in Chapter 4 because of this?

Picture your career

Having a mental picture of how your working life has progressed, especially if you want to make major changes, gives you a clear basis from which you can move on. You can visualise the picture changing in some way, according to your own vision, your hopes and dreams for the future. You can picture your own working life so far in a number of ways:

The Life's Work Tree

This is the career of someone who has done the same work all his life from a small beginning, like an acorn developing into an oak tree, growing along pre-determined lines. It could be a business that has grown over the years, or a professional skill that he has consistently developed, so that by the end of his career, he may be 'at the top of the tree' in his chosen field. This may have involved a very detailed strategy or training.

Snakes and Ladders

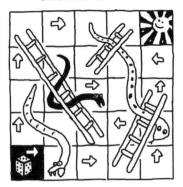

This career picture is where someone has climbed up a ladder, progressing up the next progressive rung, through promotion or skills training for example. Sometimes he has reached the top of a ladder and there is nowhere else to climb. Sometimes redundancy or changes in the organisation have seen him sliding down the snake, only to find himself at some point on a new ladder. His strategy will probably have been about the next step and not much further beyond. The ladders could be different functions, for example marketing or accounts, and the size of them may be related to the size of the organisation.

Portfolio Career

The portfolio career represents the working life of someone with many skills and interests that all seem to fit together in some way. His career becomes multi-faceted. He can be self-assured and keep developing himself by learning new skills or visiting a new environment. The portfolio person can choose which skills to apply in his next setting. His strategy will have been very wide and flexible and may encompass his whole life, and not just his work. He knows how to transfer skills from home to work and work to home.

Drifting Rafts

This is the career of someone who has never really planned at all. He has drifted along with the tide and occasionally bumped into another raft which he has chosen to hop onto. Sometimes the raft has drifted on calm waters and sometimes it has felt like a 'white water ride', in which he clung on as the raft was swept along. Usually he will not have had any strategy.

Create your own picture or symbol of the working life you might choose to have in future. It may help that vision come true.

Striking your balance

A quarter of all working men in Britain work more than 48 hours a week and nearly a fifth of unskilled and manual workers work more than 50 hours. A new phrase has emerged for the millennium: 'presenteeism', which is the opposite of 'absenteeism' – it basically means that many people are working harder than may be good for their health – they just won't go home! Another phrase often used these days is 'workaholic'. Many men may be working so hard that they don't really get enough time to spend on the very reasons they are working: their family, friends, children and so on.

Peter Baker and Mick Cooper, authors of *The MANual, complete man's guide to life,*[1] have worked out a simple and effective questionnaire to help you decide whether or not you are a workaholic. Ask yourself the following:

- Do you regularly bring work home or do you often work in your free time?
- Do you work more than 50 hours a week on average?
- Do you often work during your lunch breaks or miss out lunches altogether?
- Do you get complaints from your partner or friends about how much time you spend on work?
- Do you feel that you're missing out on other parts of your life – perhaps spending time with your children or partner, sport or exercise, cultural activities – because of the amount of time and energy you devote to work?
- Do you feel bored, guilty, or at a loose end when you're not working?
- Do you have few interests outside of work?
- If your boss asked you to attend an important meeting after you'd already arranged to take your partner out for a birthday meal, would you turn down your partner rather than disappoint your boss?
- If you had to describe yourself in one word, would it be your occupation?
- Are the major goals in your life work-related?

If you have answered 'yes' to three or more questions, then you may have workaholic tendencies. If you answered 'yes' to six or more questions, then workaholism could well be an issue seriously worth thinking about.

You may feel you are at the other end of the spectrum – you know you could work harder and put yourself out a bit more for your work, but you haven't bothered to.

If you answered 'no' or 'never' to all of the questions in Baker and Cooper's workaholism questionnaire, then you may need to consider engaging *more* with your work.

Now ask yourself: Is the balance between your work and other aspects outside your life:

Too much on other activities		About right		Too much on work
1	2	3	4	5

What action can you consider in the light of this?
For instance, asking for that holiday time I'm owed and booking a holiday in my diary right now. Volunteering for some project work at the next team meeting.

Different ways to work

Part of getting your balance right with work might be to consider the other options of working available to you. Work is not just an 'on-off' switch – either you work full time, long hours or you are unemployed. Very often this is an area which women seem more inclined to consider than men, and this might be why, according to government figures in 1995, 70% of new jobs go to women (source: *Independent Magazine*), because the jobs on offer these days tend to involve more flexible working practices.

It could be that you have an attitude that any work except full-time work brands you as a 'light weight'. You might hear the old saying 'Jack of all trades, master of none', which may hold you back from doing flexible, portfolio-type work. But evidence of these working patterns may be exactly the sort of thing that is getting people jobs these days.

You might also like to ask yourself whether you would be prepared to consider being a 'career-parent', if your partner is able to earn the sustaining wage. Many more men are considering this option. The 'New Man' may be a myth but the 'new dad' is not. Despite longer working hours, men's involvement with their children is

111

increasing steadily: on average men spend 16 minutes a day on childcare in the UK compared to 3 minutes in 1961.

If you have kids, you may not want to be the at-home parent full time but would like some time at home with your children on an ongoing basis, especially around the time of their birth. What about paternity leave?

By law, in the UK in 2005 all fathers are entitled to up to 2 weeks paid paternity leave, taken in one block, up to 56 days after your child's birth. You must have been employed consecutively by the same employer for 26 weeks in order to qualify.

Unfortunately though, only one in five eligible fathers is using the statutory paid paternity leave entitlement, according to government figures quoted on the Fathers Direct website, correct as at July 2005. (www.fathersdirect.com)

The Department of Trade and Industry forecast that in the first year of new fathers being eligible for a fortnight's paid leave, 80% of the 400,000 workers affected would take it up. But figures for the year to April 2004 suggest just 79,000 used their entitlement. Perhaps men are frightened of demonstrating a lack of dedication to their workplace by focusing on their parental responsibilities? Yet a report sponsored by Carlton TV [2] says that men who are closely involved as fathers are more (not less!) likely to be successful at work than less-involved fathers.

Parental leave is also offered in many other EU countries and Australia, and by some employers. This is more than extended paternity leave; it is the right to some time off for childcare after the time of the birth, on an ongoing basis. This can be up to 3 months leave a year, taken as a block or in small chunks of time, with your job held open for your return.

According to the 'New Ways to Work' survey, more flexible working patterns increased men's motivation and energy as well as enabling them to spend more time with their families and friends. The same survey showed that men who spend more time with their children became better at time management, listening and negotiating skills, which are exactly the sort of skills employers say they look for in new recruits.

Use the different ways you have worked and your different life experiences, for example your experience of part-time project management, your experience of teaching your daughter to read, as marketable skills actually advancing your job prospects rather than holding you back.

The trade-off   With many of these alternative working options, there may be a trade-off, financially and possibly also in terms of your self-esteem. If you worked part-time, you may take home less money, but you might still earn enough for your needs; and this trade-off may be worth the extra time you gain to do other things. Similarly, if you did the home work whilst your partner worked, you may feel 'less of a man' at first, but you may feel your quality of life is enhanced by having much more contact with your growing children. And you may be surprised when your mates stop taking the mickey and start to envy you not having to fight your way through traffic to the office.

As Vincent Foster, one-time US Presidential adviser, said: *'No one was ever heard to say on their deathbed, "I wish I had spent more time at the office!"'*

These different ways to work are all options available to you.

What other ways of working would you like to consider?

What would be the advantages and disadvantages?

You and your organisation

IS YOUR ORGANISATION...	...OR IS IT?
Rational, well-ordered and purposeful	Irrational, chaotic and emotional
Someone else's problem	Everybody's responsibility
There to give you a living	Return participation with rewards
A secular institution, devoid of heart or soul	A sacred place imbued with a soul
Where you earn the means to live	Where we live much of our lives
One needing to be directed and driven from the top	One possessing innate energy and purpose at every level
Simple closed systems	Complex, open, dynamic systems
One working according to simple material laws	One working according to complex human laws
Defined in term of profit and loss	Defined in terms of the human relationships within them
Existing for its own sake	Existing as part of a community

Understanding the organisation that you work in or want to work in can give you better chances of job satisfaction and help you set clearer goals for advancement if that is what you want.

Most organisations today have very tight money margins to work within. That means they generally expect more and more from their employees. Sometimes it may feel that they don't just want the sweat from your brow, they want your heart and soul as well! In that case, you are looking for something extra in return. In surveys, 90% of employees say they want more training and development. Organisations are responding by offering more opportunities for education and leisure than ever before.

Audit your organisation

Look closely at your organisation as a whole, its values, products, services, and methods, and decide for yourself whether you approve or not. And if not, what are you going to do towards making any changes?

Conduct your own audit, an inspection of your organisation as an overview for yourself. If you are currently looking for work, answer these questions in terms of the sort of organisation you would like to work for.

YOUR ORGANISATION — AN AUDIT

What does your organisation do, make, or sell in the widest sense?

How much do you like or support this/these product(s)?

What, if any, is your organisation's 'mission statement' or purpose? How much do you agree with it? How would you change it?

Who owns your organisation, ultimately? Is it a public company, trade union, multinational, private partnership, local or national government body, etc?

What is the history of the organisation?

Where is the organisation going?

What is the overall structure of the organisation?

What are the main health and safety issues about your workplace and in the organisation generally? How good is the organisation at dealing with them?

How much of an equal opportunity employer is this organisation in practice do you think? What is your evidence for thinking this?
For instance, policies and practices that support women, different racial groups, religious groups, disabled people, gay men etc.

What flexible employment initiatives, such as internal secondments, job sharing etc., are supported in practice by your organisation? (Again, give evidence)

What is highly valued in practice?
For instance, loyalty, bright ideas, training, long service etc.

What would you most like to change about your organisation as a whole?

How could you personally make the first steps towards this change in your area or department?

Overall, how does the culture of your work affect you and your ability to achieve your ambitions?

Changing organisations   There are many different trends facing organisations including:

- Pressure on staff at all levels now that many organisations have 'downsized'
- Flatter organisational structures with fewer immediately evident stages for promotion
- Technological advances are speeding up
- Increased competition and opportunity since the opening of the single European market and globalisation generally
- Reorganisation and restructuring is an ongoing process as organisations strive to be more flexible
- Greater increase in environmental pressures, awareness and responsibility
- More flexible working patterns, reducing the number of full time employees and contracting more work to freelance people and small businesses
- Regular cycles of recession and mini-boom mean constant change in levels of skill shortages
- Demonstrating an increased concern with local community involvement, schools, nationwide appeals, sporting and cultural sponsorship etc.
- The 'career for life' concept is increasingly obsolete
- Privatisation of major sectors of the public sector
- Increased financial accountability is being required of individual departments, units and managers

---

In 1995, The Equal Opportunities Commission predicted 300,000 fewer jobs in the traditionally 'male' sectors of building, engineering, and manufacturing by the year 2000, whilst 500,000 new jobs will be created in service- and information technology-related sectors, more likely to be filled by women. However by 2005 another more complex pattern had emerged, that of skills shortages in traditionally 'gendered' occupations. In engineering or construction for example, where the culture seems to be less attractive or welcoming to women, there are major skills shortages, and similarly, in traditionally 'female' occupations such as childcare, a similar pattern of skills shortage emerges, yet a reluctance of men to enter these sectors. In 2005:

- *Women make up just one per cent of employment in construction occupations*
- *Women account for only eight per cent of employment in engineering occupations*
- *Almost all nursery nurses and childminders are female.*

What all of these trends mean is that there are great opportunities, for those with the right skills and flexible attitudes. Unskilled workers with a rigid attitude towards the sort of work they will do and how they will do it will be less able than ever to find a satisfactory job.

117

Diana Mather, author of *Image Works for Men,*[3] says that there are four basic qualities that all employers are looking for beyond qualifications and a track record. They are:

1. **Resourcefulness** – ability to seek solutions under their own steam
2. **Resilience** – stamina and ability to cope well with and introduce good change
3. **Responsibility** – evidence of taking responsibility for things both inside and outside of work
4. **Vision** – not taking things for granted, and a sense of how things might go

Which of these qualities have you got?

Which ones could you develop?

Which organisational trends have directly affected you or people you know?

How?

What opportunities do they offer you?

What threat do they pose you?

⌐*How will they influence the important people in your work life?*

⌐*How will they influence the important people in your personal life?*

Gaining recognition

Think of the organisation you work for as a resource for you to use for your development, and not just in terms of promotion. Take into account different possible steps available to you, including sideways moves, relocating to new departments and parts of the world, training in new skills, undertaking different projects and so on.

Job security is regarded by many as a thing of the past. There is no doubt that the world's fast-changing economic cycles mean very few jobs are 'guaranteed for life', but it may be a bit of a myth that they ever were. These days, security comes from two places: firstly from within, in terms of how prepared you are for change, and secondly in terms of your ability to make it clear to others what your achievements are.

Looking at that second factor, consider some statistics from research conducted by Harvey Coleman (ex-IBM) across a large number of organisations.

Three factors were identified that determine whether someone got promoted or not:

1. **Performance** – the reality of how good your work actually is.

2. **Image** – the impression you create about yourself and your work. We all know of people who were overlooked for promotion because, while their work was actually good, they gave the impression of being confused, unable to cope or not interested in moving on,

3. **Visibility** – whether people know of you. This means raising your profile, becoming more visible and building your contacts. You may do a great job, have a great image, but if the right people don't know that you exist, you won't get promoted.

119

The contribution of each of these factors to people being promoted was:

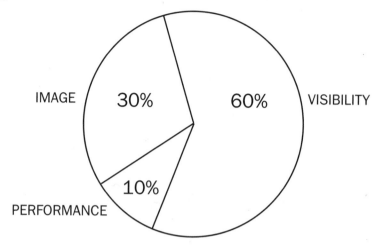

You may have strong feelings about the fact that the quality of your work may only contribute 10% towards getting you promotion, but if you're in an organisation where there are lots of people doing a good job, the other two factors naturally assume greater and greater significance. So keep doing a good job.

Think about it from your point of view – who do you notice in the workplace? Do you tend to notice the people who do a great job or are you generally so busy and tuned in to your own area that you only notice people who actively raise their visibility with you? This state of affairs is natural when most people are very engrossed in what they are doing.

What this is *not* saying is: 'Don't bother working hard' or 'Don't think anyone will notice you for doing it well'! What this is saying is: 'Do a good job and make sure that you gain recognition for it, by building a sound image and putting some energy into your visibility.'

You might want to consider your image and visibility in more detail in Chapter 13: Getting Yourself Across.

Your personal power

As part of your strategy towards your work, you might like to consider how much power you actually have in your role. This isn't about your ability to manipulate people or manoeuvre situations solely to your advantage! This is about the legitimate influence you can express, as part of your rightful position.

Power comes with responsibilities as much as privileges.

This 'power' means more than just what position you hold. Your power is your ability to influence others, and according to Dr. Margaret Ryan,[4] there are at least four dimensions to this influence:

1. **Formal Authority** – The power invested in you by your job title, your official role.

2. **Expertise** – This is the power given to you by your specialist knowledge, skills, qualifications etc. The more exclusive the expertise and the more useful in your workplace, the more power it gives you.

3. **Resource control** – This is the power you may have in the control of physical, financial or informational resources. For example: allocation of car parking spaces, access to the stationery cupboard, access to people and events (such as Trade Union meetings) etc. The most valued resources are often money and information. Actually the most *valuable* resource is people!

4. **Interpersonal skills** – This is the power you have to communicate with people, get on with them, and to build good-quality relationships. This can be the most potent form of power, and in its most obvious form is sometimes called 'charisma'. Contrary to what many may think, the starting point of this skill is the ability to listen to others. For most people, this is an underdeveloped resource of power and influence, an untapped resource.

Even if you do not necessarily face avenues by means of which you can develop your influence in formal ways (no.1), there may well be ways in which you can use the facilities open to you to develop yourself in terms of 2, 3 or 4, especially if you can provide evidence for ways in which this will benefit those with whom you work.

Bearing this in mind:

What formal authority does your role give you?
For instance, the people you supervise, the responsibilities you have, the freedom to make decisions etc.

In what ways could you develop your formal authority in future?

What sort of expertise, specialist knowledge, skills etc. does someone need to do your job?
For instance, professional qualification, knowledge of the sector or market, contacts etc.

In what ways could you continue to develop your expertise?

What resources can you give or withhold access to?
For instance, money, information, ideas, training, other people, computers, equipment, perks, time etc.

What resources would you like to take more responsibility for?

What evidence can you provide of your greatest strengths in terms of your interpersonal skills at work? For instance, I listened to my colleague's concerns about the recent system changes and acted upon them.

Which of the following areas of interpersonal skill could you develop more?
- Listening to the views of others
- Networking with people of all types and levels
- Gaining the confidence of others
- Speaking at meetings
- Being assertive rather than passive or aggressive
- Negotiating
- Others – add

Power with responsibility

Using your power in a way that fits in with your values and integrity is important. Then you can use it with responsibility.

Having the formal authority, expertise or resource control may not be enough. Being seen to use it responsibly is important. Other people's willingness to be influenced hinges largely on the impression you create.

What will you do to express your power responsibly?

A New Ways to Work survey showed that more flexible working patterns increased men's motivation and energy as well as enabling them to spend more time with their families and friends. This survey also said that men who spend more time with their children become better at time management, listening and negotiating skills.

'If a 40 year-old man buys a lottery ticket at 7.55pm, he stands a better chance of having a fatal heart attack by the time of the draw on the hour than he does of winning the lottery.'

'A 35-year-old male should be paying 12.5% of his monthly salary into a scheme to secure a pension of half to two-thirds of final salary.'

Quotes courtesy of *Men's Health Magazine*

Where do you want to go now?

Think about:
– adding to the notes section, where you can record any useful ideas in the blank pages at the end of the workbook
– deciding which chapter to go to next

Philip – Birmingham

Past

I came from a broken home with a violent and abusive father. My mother was and is my rock.

Present

I am a chubby, slightly odd-looking forty-year-old, who is passionate about books and aviation. I am married with one child in a secure job.

Future

Being remembered as an enthusiastic and considerate member of society. Retiring from my present job and riding off into my dotage on a Harley Davidson with sidecar.

8

Being with Others

" *This above all: to thine own self be true,*
and it must follow, as the night the day,
thou canst not then be false to any man* "

Shakespeare – *Hamlet*

* Or, of course, woman!

Objectives
- To look at your relationships and to choose how you can build on them and divide your time amongst them
- To understand yourself better by looking at the pattern of your relationships

This chapter is important because
- Like cars, relationships break down if they're not well maintained
- Relationships can be the antidote to isolation
- Good relationships help you celebrate the good times and support you through the difficult times

Content
- Relationships – the bigger picture
- Time for your relationships
- Types of relationships
- Other relationships that matter

Relationships – the bigger picture

You may have many kinds of relationships:

- Friendship
- Life partnerships
- Sexual relationships
- Family relationships
- Acquaintances
- Adversaries
- Work colleagues
- Team-mates
- Neighbours
- Correspondences by letter, fax, e-mail
- Yourself
- Others

This chapter examines the time you spend on relationships and helps you to think through what your priorities are and how important relationships are to you. It's about maximising the benefits from being in relationships and gaining the understanding to meet the challenges that relationships bring.

Relationships are your network of connections and this network covers a very wide range of different people. Relationships can be like a cinema screen onto which you project yourself and your personality. This makes them valuable learning tools.

If you have adversaries, your relationship with them will also tell you something about yourself.

You can tell a lot about yourself by your relationships.

Men and intimacy

Men are no less 'good at intimacy' than women. They just apply higher standards of 'feeling safe' before they'll reveal themselves. Research has found that 'where men and women feel safe from conflict early in their relationship, their communication in terms of intimacy tends to be equivalent'.

Source: Clements ML et al.[1]

Radiators and drains

Think about:

- Some people will be radiators – they will radiate confidence, energy and support and help build you up.
- Some people will be drains – they will drain your energy away,

sometimes by being over-confident and putting you down, or by being under-confident and relying on you to carry them through.

Time for your relationships

Think about this question: Is the balance right for you in terms of how much time you make for the important relationships in your life?

- A balance between time for yourself and time for others? Too far towards the former can lead to isolation and loneliness – too much towards the latter may lead to dependence or a feeling of suffocation.
- A balance between work relationships and those at home? Too much one way may lead to important support being withdrawn from the other side.
- A balance of friends and family? Too much one way and pressure could be exerted from the other side, or from within you.

Dividing your time

What is the balance for you now?

Divide up the circle below into a 'pie chart' of your life, with each slice depicting the amount of time you estimate you put into your relationships, right now, with:

- *Work colleagues, voluntary work colleagues*
- *Friends*
- *Partner*
- *Children*
- *Family*
- *Yourself*
- *Church and/or spiritual contacts*
- *Others*

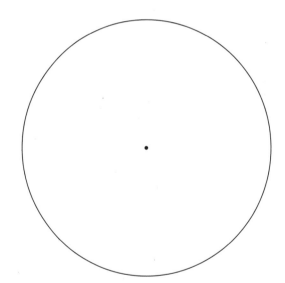

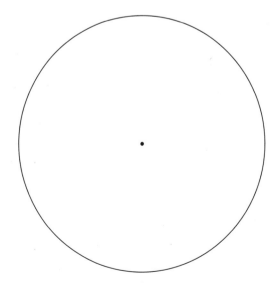

Now divide this pie chart again, depicting how you would like the situation to be ideally in the future:

Take a look at what you've drawn – what are the major differences between the two charts?

What would you like to change about how you spend your time?

These could become further goals for your strategy. (See Chapter 5 – Setting goals that work, page 71).

In all your relationships:

You may have much more choice and freedom than you think.

Only you can tell in the end what changes will be for the best.

Types of relationships

Broadly speaking your relationships can fall into four categories: close, casual and influential.

- Close relationships – give meaning to your life, e.g. life partner
- Casual relationships – give a background to your life, e.g. fellow team supporters
- Influential relationships – give your life direction, and in which you give direction to others, e.g. mentor
- Friends – how about them? How often do you see them? What is the difference for you between a friend and an acquaintance? How would you feel if you spent more time with your friends? What can and can't you talk about with them?

Each of these types of relationships may have certain characteristics already, and some characteristics that you feel may be missing. What's missing may become part of your goal strategy.

According to University of Essex ESRC research, men spend 'considerably more time' with their children than their parents' or grandparents' generation.
- *2% of families are male single-parented*
- *90% of men now choose to be present at the birth of their children*

In a Gallup survey, 35% of men aged 20-35 said that they had children mainly because their partner wanted them.

- *5 years post-separation, 2 out of 3 children see their out-of-home parent rarely, which in 90% of cases is their father*
- *90% of married men never do the ironing*
- *57% of men have done some DIY in the past four weeks*

Relationships with women

Men can have a wide range of relationships with women. They can be our mothers, sisters, daughters, partners, colleagues, lovers and friends. There is a lot of publicity about the so-called 'battle of the sexes', from both sides.

If you want to be happy, there is no need for there to be a 'war' or 'struggle'. Your relationships with women can involve open, mutually respectful communication.

This means respect comes from both sides. Recognition of the different needs and motivations can simply make life more interesting.

It is often said that there is a male side and a female aspect in all of us. This may change in different situations. The differences between being a 'man' and a 'woman', are firstly the obvious physical, genetic, differences. Scientists have identified more tendency to aggression in boys than girls as early as two years old. Secondly, differences may be programmed into you by your upbringing; that is, by the experience of your relationship with women close to you when you were growing up. That is to say, boys are 'taught' to be boys and girls are 'taught' to be girls.

But in a world in which the expectations placed upon men and women are changing very fast, these lessons about differences can be as much a hindrance as a help in our relationships with each other.

For example, if you were taught that:

- to open doors for women was the sign of being a 'gentleman', you may feel justifiably confused if now that behaviour is regarded as 'sexist' and unacceptable
- a 'woman's place is in the home', then you may have difficulties relating well to a powerful woman boss

129

- boys don't cry, then you may feel odd or embarrassed when you do

These are just examples of where the old ways may be out of date. You are not 'wrong' if you hold on to them, but they may not be good survival tools in today's world.

Thinking about this, what are your assumptions, your beliefs about women that you bring with you into your relationships with them? Write some of them down here:

How far are these useful or appropriate in today's world?

It could also be that some of the women you know have equally inappropriate beliefs about men! For example: One woman you know may think that men don't have any feelings. This could contribute to the 'battle of the sexes' as well.

What assumptions do you think the women you know make about men?

What do you want to challenge, if anything, about these assumptions?

Some of the key choices you have in relating to women around you may be in terms of these beliefs or preconceptions that you hold. You may also want to negotiate with them about their beliefs about men as part of the same process.

Communication – Vive la différence!

Men and women do have different patterns of communication. Understanding the differences and taking account of them in communications makes for better relationships.

> But men and women are more alike than different in terms of how they communicate.
>
> Deborah Tannen – *You just don't Understand*

A survey was conducted by the psychologist James J. Forest,[2] of the top 15 words most likely to appeal to men and women reading best-selling 'self-help' books. They were:

	For women	For men
1	self	self
2	communication	attitude
3	attitude	life
4	life	communication
5	understand	family
6	talking	talking
7	problems	problems
8	family	love
9	expectations	understand
10	friends	behaviour
11	emotional	people
12	feel	emotional
13	relationship	responsibility
14	love	control
15	parents	sense

Note:
- The two lists have 10 words in common. (That's over 65%)
- The odd words out were:
  - for **women**: expectations, friends, feel, relationships and parents
  - for **men**: behaviour, people, responsibility, control and sense

Is it your experience that women tend to communicate their *feelings* in *relationships* based on *expectations*, with *friends* and *parents*? Whereas men tend to emphasise, in communication, how *people behave,* in terms of their *sense* of *responsibility* and *control*?

131

If you want to improve your relationships with women, pay attention to the differences in communication. They may be smaller than you think, but they may also be significant.

What would you like to change about your communication or relationships with the women you know?

What could be your first step?

What would you like women you know to do differently?

Relationships with men   Your relationships with men may fall into certain patterns, again according to your upbringing and experience. It may be that there are some things you can do and talk about with your male friends and some things you would not do or talk about.

What are these?

Things I do and talk about with my male friends:

Things I don't do/talk about with my male friends:

What are the advantages and disadvantages of this situation?

Advantages:

Disadvantages:

Why do you think the pattern has evolved this way?

Is it how you really want it to be, or do you fall into that pattern because:
* *That is what they expect*
* *That is what you've both/all been taught*
* *You'd feel uncomfortable if it was different*
* *They'd feel uncomfortable if it was different*
* *Any other reason?*

In *Men are from Mars, Women are from Venus,*[3] John Gray says that men often have a 'cave' – that is a private 'internal' space into which they go to work things out, rather than talking things through with friends and partners, which can be more a woman's style.

What issues do you

– *take to your 'cave'?*

– *talk over with male friends/family?*

– *talk over with female friends/family?*

You will benefit from getting into the habit of seeing men as a supportive resource rather than just an area of competition. It will give you more options.

What are the unique qualities and support your male friends can offer you?

What might you like to change about your relationships with male friends?

How might you make the first step?

Relationships with family

You can change your friends... but you can't change your family. However, you can change your attitude to your family members.

For many people, family relationships can be filled with the extremes of feeling, from wonderfully loving to terrifyingly abusive. Your family relationships are important in terms of where you come from, but they are not by any means the be-all and end-all of who you are or where you end up.

For example, your father and mother formed you biologically, and in many ways may have influenced you mentally and emotionally, but you are also your own person, are here for your own reasons, and have your own life to lead.

It is good to take stock of these relationships and decide for yourself if there is anything you might like to change about them. Of course, 'It takes two to tango' and you may not be able to get them to change, but at least you will be clearer about your own feelings and intentions.

Looking at relationships with key people, even if they are dead, may resolve issues you have with them by understanding the impact they have had on you.

Mothers   It is said: 'You will always be your mother's baby'. Sometimes this is hard for a man of any age to accept. Equally it may be hard for your mother to realise that you do not wear short trousers anymore, except for football practice.

What are, or were, the characteristics of your relationship with your mother?

Is there anything about this you would like to change?

How might she respond?

What can you do about this?

In what ways might you be the same as your mother?

Fathers   Fathers often get a bad press these days. He may have been absent when you were growing up, he may have been a wonderful fun Dad or perhaps his influence was overbearing and dominant. Being a father is not an easy job in a society where the role is changing so quickly.

What are, or were, the characteristics of your relationship with your father?

Is there anything about this you would like to change?

How might he respond?

What can you do about this?

In what ways might you be the same as your father?

Other relations Sisters, brothers, grandparents, aunts and uncles, nephews and nieces, and so on all form a great potential source of delight or woe in our lives. You may find it harder to see them as individuals, just as you may feel they see you only in terms of the role you play in the family. Try to see your family for who they really are.

What family relationships are significant for you?

Are there any you may tend to overlook?

How might they be improved?

What can you do about this?

Relationships with children

A father can have a very positive influence on an infant. First-born children who have close, positive relationships with their fathers adjust better when a new baby is born.[4] And, in later life, these children are likely to get on well.[5]

Want to be close to your baby? What are the most important factors? Think about your relationship with its mother: when mothers and fathers get on well in the last three months before their baby is born, fathers are more likely to be caring for, and playing with, their babies a lot when they are six months old.[6]

Research shows that some men are spending more time than ever before with their children, whilst other men are living apart from their children, and having time with them can be difficult. Yet this does not mean they are spending more time with children on the whole. Indeed it seems that there are many places in society where men and children are becoming strangers. In the UK, for example, primary school teachers are much more likely to be women, and so are social workers and other people in the 'caring professions'.

> *21% of families are headed by lone parents*
> *Only 10% of lone parent families are headed by men*

According to government figures, girls out-perform boys at GCSE exam level in all but one local authority in the UK.[7] Could one of the reasons why girls are 'out-performing' boys at school be that boys don't get enough contact with male role models?

137

The reasons for this may be quite complex, but the fact that men and children seem to be in some way estranged could be a significant factor.

What might you get out of good relationships with children?

- A sense of meaning – what matters in life
- Fun and playfulness
- Getting things into perspective
- A sense of humour
- The rewards of parenting and influencing
- Remembering what it was like to be a child yourself
- What else?

Children are individuals too. You will naturally find it easier to get on with some than others. And teenagers may need to rebel. Remember what it was like to go through that emotional roller-coaster transition from child to adult yourself.

What is important for you about your relationship with children – your own and/or others?
With sons/boys:

With daughters/girls:

If you have children, how might you be a different or better father to them?

If you have no children or no contact with children, what would you like to change about this situation?

From *Raising Boys* by Steve Biddulph:[8]

Dads do matter

Many people ask: Do Dads matter – can't mothers do it all? The research supporting the importance of dads is overwhelming. Boys with absent fathers are statistically more likely to be violent, get hurt, get into trouble, do poorly in schools and be members of teenage gangs in adolescence. Fatherless daughters are more likely to have low self-esteem, to have sex before they really want to, get pregnant, be assaulted and not continue their schooling.

Living with people

Whoever you live with, and whether you live on your own or not, the people around you in your place of residence are usually influential relationships, ones which are important to get 'right' from time to time. This could be about:

- A flatmate who doesn't contribute to the housekeeping
- A neighbour whose music keeps you awake
- Your partner's habits that annoy or irritate you

The British Isles are crowded islands, some of the most densely populated places in the world, and so living with and around other people is a skill everybody needs.

Living with people can be draining or energising. Where there is conflict or friction, aim to base any solution on a fair deal for both sides. Your issues may seem trivial to others, but are important to you. So get them sorted!

This might be where your assertiveness and negotiation skills (see Chapter 13) come in most handy.

What are the particular issues you have, living with and around other people?

What can you constructively do about this?

⌐ *What do you want them to do differently?*

⌐ *What can you do differently?*

⌐ *If you live on your own, how do you feel about being on your own?*

Partners   Close personal relationships and partnerships involve a much wider variety of meanings and roles today than in previous generations, where they simply meant marriage, for better or for worse.

This diversity offers greater opportunities as well as pressure. The opportunities are for a more flexible lifestyle, such as long-term relationships outside of marriage, short-term relationships and same-sex relationships. Having a life partner does not necessarily mean living with her or him.

This modern flexibility also gives more men and women permission *not* to have a close partnership if they don't want one. Any close relationship/partnership is always changing as you are always changing. It may be the different speeds or directions of change in the two halves that often cause the problems.

What are the ups and down of your partnership, if you have one?

In what ways have you both changed since you first got together?

What can you do differently to improve your relationship?

What do you want him or her to do differently?

If you do not have a partner – is this by choice? If not, how do you feel about not having a partner?

Sex   Sex seems to bring up a lot of difficulties and extremes for many people. Maybe that is because our society puts so much emphasis upon it. But how important is it, really, for you? Men are supposed to want it all the time. You may or you may not. This is not any proof of your being more or less of a man.

Whatever you feel now about sex, as you get older your feelings may change. So what does sex mean to you? Is it about:

- Intimacy, closeness
- Attraction
- Flirtation
- Sharing
- Sensuality

141

- Massage
- Physical expression
- Lust
- Comradeship
- Virility
- Power
- Physical superiority

It can be all of these things, and more. This is an indication of how complex an issue it is.

But all of these things can also be expressed independently, as nothing to do with sex.

Which of these qualities do you only look for in sex?

Where else might you find them?

What do you most enjoy about sex?

What do you like least about it?

What are your future hopes and plans when it comes to sex?

Whatever men might say about sex in public, for most it is a complex and often difficult issue.

Other relationships that matter

There are many other things you can have connection with, besides people. Your home, for example, is a living space with which you have a relationship. Like human relationships, this one takes maintenance and a bit of 'tender loving care' to keep it satisfactory.

You may feel:

- Very comfortable with the way it is
- Worried about its state of health
- Urged to change or alter it in some way
- Desperate to move away from it
- Driven to give it more time and attention.

Who makes the decisions when it comes to your home? Decisions like:

- Where you live

- How it is furnished

- How it is decorated

- How the garden or exterior are maintained

- Any other aspects of it

Are you happy with the way it is decorated or furnished? What would you change about where you live?

What is the division of labour in your home?

– *Who does the long-term jobs like DIY and decorating?*

– *Who does the short-term essentials, like cooking, washing up, ironing, cleaning and so on?*

– *Is everybody happy with this division of labour?*

– *How could it shift?*

What else can you do to improve your relationship with your home?

You may have a hobby, activity or thing you care about with which you have a type of relationship. It could be a pet, or an old car you are cherishing, a beautiful garden or suchlike. Again, these are 'relationships' that reward the work you put into them with satisfaction, even relaxation, and a sense of purpose.

What are these for you?

What do you like about it?

What could you do differently with it?

How can you maintain and improve this relationship?

If you don't have such a connection, you could develop one. For so many people it is very rewarding.

Relationship with higher beings

Despite the decline in church membership in recent years, many people believe in some form of deity. When asked in 1998 about their religious beliefs, over one in five people agreed with the statement 'I know God really exists and I have no doubts about it' while only one in ten people said they did not believe in God. In the same survey people were asked about other religious beliefs. One in two people said they definitely or probably believed in life after death while about one in three said that they definitely or probably did not. About half of people professed a lack of belief in religious miracles.[9]

A chapter on relationships would not be complete without acknowledging that many people from a wide variety of backgrounds, belief systems, cultures and religions have yet another relationship: one to the spiritual world. Even if you have no such belief or certainty yourself you may find that understanding other people's spiritual point of view will make relationships easier and possibly more meaningful.

You can also check out your deeper sense of yourself against the following much simplified range of points.

For some people there is only a physical sense of themselves and for others there is a sense, and to some a fact, of their being a soul and a spirit as well, or a higher self which is different from your day-to-day self.

What do you believe about yourself?

For others there is a sense or a clear belief that there is one God, creator, supreme being or many Gods, devas or other spiritual beings, such as angels or archangels. For many there are distinct differences between a belief in a spiritual world and a religion. For others the two are intertwined. Others have no relationship to a spiritual world at all. Some people believe that there is only one life that you live once on this earth, and others may be certain that we live more than one life and that what we do in this life affects our next ones. As with values in an earlier chapter, only you can decide what you believe and what you feel about such ideas or facts.

Call your beliefs or lack of them what you will. One senior manager in a large retail bank put it:

'When I've got things to sort out in my head I put on my hiking boots, and go sit on a hill top and talk to the Big One upstairs.'

He uses the outdoors and the sense of a higher being to help him get things back into perspective and find some inner peace.

How do you relate to matters spiritual

– For yourself?

– When others have different beliefs?

How does having common or different beliefs affect your relationship with that person or those people?

Relationship with nature

A close relationship with the countryside and nature can be a very rewarding and grounding experience, helping to keep you physically and mentally healthy and to keep things in perspective. You can learn many things by watching the natural world, and it can give you a motivating sense of harmony and wonder.

Try looking up at the stars once in a while. You are looking at infinity – literally – there is no end to it. What better way to keep your own problems and cares in some perspective?

This doesn't just mean watching David Attenborough's nature programmes on the television, with a can of beer and your feet up. It may be that you have to put your boots on and go out and look at it for yourself.

Whatever your spiritual or religious persuasion, and even it you don't have one, there can be no harm in getting into the habit of taking reflective walks, in the countryside or even just around the block. This is one relationship in which you can usually find exactly what answers you are looking for.

More and more people are doing this kind of thing to form a direct relationship with the greater scheme of things. It could just be the quiet secret of your own success.

What could you do more of to develop your relationship with the bigger picture?

What might stop you?

How could you get over this?

What benefit would it bring you in the long run?

See yourself in your relationships

Look back at the answers you have given in this section, and sum up, being totally fair to yourself, what picture they give of the sort of person you are. Look for the positive qualities as much as, if not more than, the negative ones.

Write down what you found here:

What might you like to change as a result of this?
For instance, challenge your negative self-belief that you are not good at relationships!

Where do you want to go now?

Think about:
– adding to the notes section, where you can record any useful ideas in the blank pages at the end of the workbook
– deciding which chapter to go to next

Alan – Midlands

Past

I came from the war years; I remember rationing, air-raid shelters, not knowing my father, sitting in the gutter eating jam doorsteps, starting school. My early years were exciting with simple games, lots of friends, lots of places to go and things to do – and getting a clout round the ear for doing them!

Present

Settled, happily married, in a job I like doing, in a house I love and like living in, doing what I like to do with the people I like most. My best characteristics are that I am obliging, tolerant, forward-looking, cautious and thoughtful – worst is that I can get on people's nerves.

Future

In three years time I will be retired from work and will have a new car, plasma screen, camper van, and time to do all the things I don't have time to do now. I would like to be remembered as some-one who has had an influence on his world and has left something tangible on the landscape and in the things he has done.

Mark Bunyan

'Saying goodbye is never easy...'

When I first started my current relationship, he was studying in Edinburgh and only came down to my flat in Greenwich once or twice a month. On Monday mornings we'd have to say goodbye in the middle of the rush hour at London Bridge Station. The choice we had was either to kiss genuinely and have to deal with the realisation afterwards that we'd 'frightened the horses' (and be seen as some kind of freak) or alternatively to make our kiss goodbye a rather formal 'statement'. Either way something that should have been a natural moment (and is so for straight people) was spoiled.

I started to think about how much worse it would be for gay men in a heightened emotional context, such as a war. When I started writing songs I made this moment into: 'I'll Always Remember You Sweetheart', a song about a soldier seeing his male lover off to fight in the First World War. One evening I performed this song and afterwards I noticed in the audience that George (a then 73-year-old friend from London) was discreetly wiping away a tear. Afterwards he asked me how I'd known about moments like the one in the song. He said that he personally had seen at least two people off in similar circumstances during the Second World War.

I'LL ALWAYS REMEMBER YOU, SWEETHEART

The old man who sits in the late firelight glow
Recalls, as life draws to an end,
When he was a young man a long time ago
And Terry Mahoney was more than a friend.
The night before Terry went off to the war,
To Belgium for country and King,
They went to the Music Hall, as oft before,
Where Gwendoline Brogden would sing:

CHORUS:

I'll always remember you sweetheart.
Take care of yourself while I'm gone.
When harsh duty calls us we have to stand fast
Whatever befalls us, we'll still have the past.
You know that I'm certain to miss you
But now comes the moment to part
And although you know I can't kiss you
I'll see you again sweetheart.

The station was crowded with sweethearts and wives
Of Tommies who fought foreign lands,
All hugging and kissing for all of their lives.
He knew he and Terry could only shake hands.
He stands beside Terry and fights back the tears
The train whistle blows all too soon...
And still he remembers, down through all these years,
How Terry was humming this tune:

(CHORUS)

The old man who sits in his ninetieth year
Regrets that lost moment once more;
How foolish convention forbade him a tear
When Terry Mahoney went off to the war.
And now in his mem'ry he hears the train hiss
And walks from the station alone.
If only he'd dared give his love one last kiss...
If only, if only he'd known...

(CHORUS)

9

Well Prepared

" *Know yourself and do more* "

Johan Quanjer

Objective	• To recognise how much you've achieved already and build on that good foundation
This chapter is important because	• You need to assess where you shine and where you need to polish • You can capitalise on what you have already got going for you • Valuing yourself will help you take more risks and achieve more
Content	• Realistic self-assessment • What you've got going for you • Your skills audit • Your qualifications • Taking control

Realistic self-assessment

A good self-assessment, one that will most likely provide a good foundation on which you can succeed, will be based on what you've done well and what you're good at as well as where you might learn more, polish up and add new skills. In other words, it is best to start with what you're good at in order to address where you need to do better.

People are much more likely to trust someone who can address, in equal measure:

- What they're good at
- Where their 'gaps' are – their areas for development

This will hold true for all situations at work, socially, with close friends, and partner, and ultimately for your own self-satisfaction and happiness.

So this section is about being very realistic in terms of your confidence, your abilities and skills. Managers inside organisations report that men tend to overestimate and women tend to underestimate their skills and abilities.

It is also very important that you get the opinions and feedback of supporters when doing this section. Realistic self-assessment is almost impossible without the objective views of others. As you do this section, you can draw on this very valuable resource.

Confidence – I'm OK and you're OK

You deserve to have a good level of confidence. You have already achieved so much in your life.

This confidence is about:

- Being able to start things feeling that you will do reasonably well
- Getting on with what you want to do
- Knowing that whatever happens, you will be OK inside yourself
- Allowing other people to get due recognition for their achievements
- 'Feeling the fear and doing it anyway'

Lack of confidence means:

- You feel you can't do things or that you will fail from the start
- You put things off until you feel better about them – which may be never!

- You have difficulty doing things
- You feel powerless or uncomfortable or both
- You feel that whatever you do, it won't be good enough
- If someone else does something well, they are skilled; if you do something well, you were lucky or got away with it
- If someone praises you, they are being patronising or perhaps they want something!
- You put yourself down in order to build others up

Over-confidence means:

- You don't know your own limitations
- You undertake to do things you can't necessarily fulfil
- You are unrealistic about what you could handle
- You think you would be better than someone else at everything
- You need to put others down in order to build yourself up

Confidence may be a key issue in your Navigator journey. Knowing the situations where you are under- or over-confident may lead to the goals you set yourself.

When you are realistically confident, you can build yourself up alongside everyone else. If you are unconfident, you may tend to see yourself negatively in terms of others. If you are over-confident, you may need to knock others down in order to maintain that false sense of yourself. And if you are really unconfident, to the point of being depressive, then everybody will be getting it wrong!

Identify your own confidence peaks and troughs here:

When do you feel most confident? – Situations, with particular people, etc

In what situations, or with which people, do you lack confidence?

In what situations may you have been over-confident?

What happened as a result?

Use the situations and people who help your confidence as the foundation stones on which to build further. When our confidence takes a knock, remember these situations, draw strength from them, and get support from those who will remind you of your abilities.

What you've got going for you

You have aspects of yourself that you could use to achieve your goals. Don't underestimate them. Put them to work for you.

Your achievements

Wherever you are on your life's journey, you will have already gained experience and have achievements under your belt. Achievements can also be about overcoming setbacks.

What achievements in your life are you really proud of?
Include all areas of your life – family, work, home, social, sports, hobbies, relationships, community activities, old achievements as well as recent ones:

1

2

3

4

5

6

7

8

9

10

When the going gets tough, remember what you have already achieved, and visualise successes like these in future.

Qualities and strengths   Knowing your qualities and strengths helps you:

- Be confident
- Choose appropriate goals
- Know when goals are achievable and realistic
- See which situations you handle well
- Tackle situations with some element of risk

Using the table on the next page:

List your strengths in the top left-hand box.

These are all the things that feel positive about you, the good qualities you have. List as many as possible. Keep coming back and adding more. Ask some supporters for their opinions if you have trouble thinking of anything.

Do the same for your weaknesses, in the bottom right-hand box.

Again, getting some feedback might be a good idea. These are qualities of your character that you feel may hold you back.

YOUR STRENGTHS	
	YOUR WEAKNESSES

Strengths and weaknesses are a balancing act

Let's suppose:
- There are no such things as weaknesses, only qualities that are out of balance
- If that's the case, then a quality becomes a strength when it is balanced for you and the situation.
- A quality becomes a weakness when it is either overdone or underdone for you and the situation.

For example: Being flexible can be strength. If you overdo being flexible, you might become aimless, which could be a weakness. If you underdo being flexible, you become rigid in your thinking, which could also be a weakness. Being impatient can be a weakness, but underlying that could be a strength: your own energy and enthusiasm to get on with something. Therefore if you tone it down a little, it can become an asset.

Go back to the previous page. In the left-hand bottom box write down the potential strength which underlies the weakness you have identified.

Here are some suggestions to help:

Underdone ←	Quality →	Overdone
Unreliable	Reliable	Stubborn
Disrespectful	Respectful	Submissive
Slow	Quick to act	Rash
Pessimistic	Positive	Unrealistic
Closed minded	Open minded	Gullible
Spineless	Determined	Ruthless
Rigid thinking	Flexible thinking	Woolly thinking
Uninterested	Interested	Nosey
Antagonistic	Impartial	Biased
Unambitious	Ambitious	Ruthless
Disorganised	Organised	Oppressive
Timid	Confident	Arrogant

Once you have found the potential strength that is being underdone or overdone, you will be able to decide on some action. For example, if you would like to appear more interested in other people and suspect you seem uninterested or aloof, you could ask a few more questions, without being a nosy parker! Or, if you want to be more confident, you can be honest with others about your room for development as well as telling them your achievements.

After you've looked at your weaknesses, use the top right-hand box to look at your strengths, just to check that you are not overdoing them.

Remember to get some feedback on this as well. Get a second opinion from a reliable source, such as a coaching partner.

Your skills audit

A skill is an ability to do something. You will feel more confident when you are doing things you are skilled at.

You will have gained very many types of skills, to a lesser or greater extent. Don't undervalue any of them.

Remember:

Success = Preparation + Opportunity

157

You never know when a rusty skill, like an old garden tool, can be brought out of the tool shed, polished up and put to good use, when the right opportunity arises. That is why you need to remember all your skills – as many as you can.

Similarly, a gap in your skills is just an opportunity to learn something that you haven't yet had the opportunity to develop.

Your skills can fit into four categories:
- Planning skills
- Doing skills
- Keeping going skills
- Evaluating skills

It makes sense to start with planning skills, even though it is the everlasting skills that will often push you to make a change.

The next pages have lists of skills for which you are asked to rate yourself. It is a good idea to get a worthwhile second opinion, so photocopy these pages twice before you start. Give these copies to at least two others, one from work and one from outside, and ask them to rate you as well. You can then compare these answers to your own.

The gaps at the bottom of each category are for you to add any other skills that you want to, such as technical skills that are specific to your work.

Rate yourself 1-5 as follows:

5 – Extremely good at this
4 – Good at this
3 – OK at this
2 – Not very good at this
1 – Not at all good at this

Planning skills   These are about the future.

Having good planning skills minimises unnecessary risks and mistakes. They are like the old machine-shop saying: 'Measure twice, cut once'. They enable you to consider options and use your pragmatic and creative qualities. Add your own ideas to the end of the list:

- ☐ Gathering information
- ☐ Interpreting information
- ☐ Organising ideas
- ☐ Categorising correctly
- ☐ Estimating
- ☐ Setting realistic objectives
- ☐ Exploring and expanding ideas
- ☐ Visualising what might happen
- ☐
- ☐

- ☐ Using my imagination
- ☐ Having ideas
- ☐ Diagnosing correctly
- ☐ Predicting accurately
- ☐ Budgeting
- ☐ Anticipating
- ☐ Assessing
- ☐ Making decisions
- ☐
- ☐

> *Our deepest fear is not that we are inadequate. Our deepest fear is that we are powerful beyond measure. It is our light, not our darkness, that most frightens us. We ask ourselves: 'Who am I to be brilliant, gorgeous, talented, fabulous?' Actually, who are you not to be?... As we are liberated from our own fear, our presence automatically liberates others.*
>
> Nelson Mandela, quoting Marianne Williamson, in his inaugural speech as President of South Africa

Doing skills

Doing skills are about the present.

Having made a plan, doing skills enable you to carry it out. They fall into three categories: doing things in relation to yourself, other people and things. They are also the technical skills you may have learned in relation to your job or in other formal ways, such as driving a vehicle.

- ☐ Using physical strength
- ☐ Using dexterity
- ☐ Using co-ordination
- ☐ Understanding instructions
- ☐ Following instructions
- ☐ Persuading/influencing others
- ☐ Enthusing
- ☐ Reading
- ☐ Writing
- ☐ Speaking
- ☐ Calculating
- ☐ Using visual awareness
- ☐ Recognising opportunities
- ☐ Computer/technology literacy
- ☐ Seeing steps to be taken
- ☐
- ☐

- ☐ Finding solutions
- ☐ Changing plans
- ☐ Taking measured risks
- ☐ Giving clear instructions
- ☐ Motivating others
- ☐ Getting things going
- ☐ Attending to detail
- ☐ Prioritising
- ☐ Using time well
- ☐ Negotiating
- ☐ Expressing feelings
- ☐ Organising resources
- ☐ Observing
- ☐ Operating machinery
- ☐ Pacing yourself
- ☐
- ☐

Add your relevant technical skills here, including work skills and others

☐ Driving ☐
☐ ☐
☐ ☐
☐ ☐

Keeping going skills

Keeping going skills enable you to persist, get the best out of every situation, and enjoy life.

☐ Knowing when to stop ☐ Helping others
☐ Knowing when to keep going ☐ Using your intuition
☐ Encouraging yourself ☐ Encouraging others
☐ Laughing, seeing the funny side ☐ Having fun
☐ Speeding up ☐ Slowing down
☐ Seeing the new in the everyday ☐ Being creative
☐ Changing plans ☐ Listening
☐ Finishing things ☐ Counselling others
☐ Coaching others ☐ Attending to detail
☐ ☐
☐ ☐

Evaluating skills

Evaluating skills are about getting the best from your past, from your experience. They enable you to learn, make decisions and make better plans next time.

☐ Assessing objectively ☐ Observing objectively
☐ Measuring results realistically ☐ Drawing conclusions
☐ Comparing results ☐ Reviewing
☐ Seeing the bigger pictures ☐ Adapting
☐ Letting go ☐ Decision making
☐ Recognising achievements ☐ Gathering opinions
☐ Identifying room for improvement ☐ Relaxing
☐ ☐
☐ ☐

What does it all mean?

Have you got more going for you than you thought, or less perhaps? Check that you are being fully realistic about your skills set. Are you being too modest? Do you have a perfectionist 'head tape' such as 'don't be boastful', that prevents you from taking full credit for what you do well?

How do your ratings compare with that of others to whom you gave copies to fill in? What are the important differences?

Use their ratings to challenge your own as they may see you more clearly than you see yourself.

Use this space for your notes of things you've learnt from this exercise:

Transferable skills

Your use of your skills could be unnecessarily limited by putting them in 'boxes' and not recognising a wide variety of situations in which you can employ them. Some skills you might use at work may be very useful in the home, and vice versa.

That is why, for example, studies have shown people who spend lots of time in child care and parenting are better at time management and communication generally, including at work. Anyone who has looked after children will know why!

As another example, a clerical officer could be described as 'just a good clerk', or as a 'multi-skilled operative', if you consider their skills set:

Understanding instructions	Getting on with people
Making decisions	Juggling tasks
Persuading others	Telephone skills
Operating machinery	Pacing time
Breaking things down	Organising people
Attention to detail	Working to deadlines
Negotiating	Encouraging others
Listening	Interpreting information
Dealing assertively with different people	
Being creative with limited resources	

MODERN SKILLS:

Love your computer

Dress up, dress down, but be yourself

Learn to do everybody else's job too

Relish your tax returns

Know your gels and mousses

Play hard

Speak plainly and clearly

Be on first name terms with the world

Have emotions

Go away for a while and relax somewhere nice

(Men's Health magazine)

Transferring your skills

As the new millennium begins, the separation between the world of work and outside is increasingly blurred. Men wanting to develop their value in a changing and more flexible workplace need to be able to transfer many skills across a wide range of situations, and help potential employers recognise just how many and varied their skills are. Flexibility is the name of the game.

For example:

- A bank clerk may want to be a marketing assistant
- A mechanic may want to become a direct services supervisor
- A factory worker may want to aim for a sales representative job
- A customer services assistant may want to be a full-time father

In each case, he would have to clearly identify the transferable skills he has in order to:

- feel confident with himself in the new role
- convince others he can do it

Write down one aspect of what you are doing now, either at work or generally, and then write alongside it all the transferable skills you can give evidence for because of this:

For instance, sorting out a mortgage involves:

Negotiating	Influencing others
Time management	Persistence
Taking risks	Keeping cool under pressure
Encouraging others	Selling myself
Strict budgeting	Knowing my limitations

Look at your skills in a transferable way. Don't limit yourself.

Your qualifications

Qualifications are a bit like a ticket into a football ground – they are needed to get past the gate, but once in the stadium, everybody has one. They can also be a double-edged sword, with people regarding you as over-qualified for some jobs. Either way, they are still an important aspect of your skills set, if not the only important thing.

Qualifications:

- Can open doors
- Can make it hard to open doors
- Give you credibility
- Come in all shapes and sizes
- Tell people what you have learnt
- Tell people what you can do
- Tell people what sort of a person you are
- Can be an asset or a hindrance
- Educational qualifications diminish in value as you get further away from when you got them
- Professional qualifications are often highly valued, but may need regular updating
- People have got to the top without qualifications

List your qualifications here:

School qualifications:

For instance, CSEs, GCSEs, GCEs, A levels, Scottish Leaving Certificates

Other qualifications taken at school:

For instance, life-saving certificates, music grades

College, polytechnic, or university qualifications:
For instance, City and Guilds, HNCs/HNDs, degrees, postgraduate, diplomas, B.TEC

Courses attended for which no formal qualifications were given at the end:

Professional/vocational qualifications
Also include courses that you're doing now

Qualifications I need/want to get in future:
Include everything, even if you don't feel certain you'll go for it

Anything else to add?

What do you feel about all your qualifications?

If you have qualifications – be proud of the work you put in. If you feel you haven't got much written down, don't worry. Many successful people have few formal qualifications.

The qualifications you had when you left school may have opened some doors but by the time you get to 25, school-leaving qualifications are no longer relevant – people are looking for more. Similarly, a degree may not mean much after ten years. You may need to take more qualifications to suit your current goals.

Ways of gaining qualifications

Think about the many ways you can gain qualifications before making future decisions. This is where your planning skills come in handy! Award-giving bodies, like everyone else, are constantly increasing their flexibility. You can consider:

- Full-time, flexi-time, part-time, block release and short courses
- Distance learning, correspondence and Open University-style courses needing little or no time away from home
- Evening, day and weekend courses
- Fixed schedule and 'take as long as you like' programmes

Which qualifications?

You don't need any formal qualifications at all to start an Open University degree course. On the other hand, even if you have a PhD, you may still need a vocational qualification to achieve your next goal. Think about a wide range of options, and ask around, before deciding which one to investigate further.

What sort of qualifications are you interested in finding out more about?

What qualification do you need or want to get for your work?

What qualifications do you need or want to get for your own fun, leisure activity or satisfaction?

You can also find out what support there is available to you, at work or from your local educational authorities, charitable trust or government. It may be the time to use your detective skills! Start by finding out:

What is the policy of your organisation with regard to vocational and other qualifications?

Taking control

Now that you have explored in depth your achievements, qualities, skills and qualifications, you may be able to see that you are capable of many things. When life offers you new challenges and hurdles to clear, you can draw on a lot of experience which says *'I've got through this before and I can do it again'*.

This is a powerful statement for taking control of your life. It is about your confidence, your skills and your attitude.

Not everything in life will be under your immediate control. For example, you might not be able to change your basic nature or physical characteristics, but you can change your attitude to these, and your ways of dealing with prejudice in others about you.

You may not be able to radically change society or the face of where you work or live (at least, not on your own). But you can change your attitude to these, by maintaining a confident profile, keeping up with changes, selling your skill sets and helping to influence others positively.

So there is quite a lot you can control in your life, depending on your attitude, your confidence, and the recognition of your capabilities. That means that a lot is really up to you.

Write down things that you want to change about your attitude towards your confidence, your achievements, skills and capabilities.
For instance, I'd like to be easier on myself and give myself a break

Where do you want to go now?

Think about:
- adding to the notes section, where you can record any useful ideas in the blank pages at the end of the workbook
- deciding which chapter to go to next

Tim – Hampshire

Past

I was moving along in a semi-directionless manner, with goals in mind, but not entirely sure whether these were my goals or other peoples' – whether I really wanted them. I grumbled about my lot, complained about my luck and was unwilling to challenge both.

Present

On the edge of a beginning, a fresh start, an adventure discovering myself and my place in my world. I am too openly honest with others, too ready to show my vulnerability, rather than parade my strengths, although I admire my own honesty.

Future

I am not sure where I want to be except that I want to be myself, and I would like to be remembered for the qualities I believe I have rather than anything I may have 'done'.

Peter Bystricky

– Stranger in a strange land

Somebody once told me that emigration is like being born again without the benefit of childhood. When I found myself in the summer of 1968 in front of the British Passport Officer telling him that I wanted to spend the rest of my life in Great Britain, I knew very little about what that really meant. The Russian tanks had overrun my home town of Prague in what was then Czechoslovakia and nobody was fighting. It was the end of the so-called 'Prague Spring'.

This time I would start again without the benefit of childhood friends, roast duck, cabbage and dumplings and without my native language. Communication was my first priority and the local college was quite obliging. As an immigrant, I had lost everything except my accent!

I had been given a chance in my new country and I was determined to take it. I guess life is about taking up new challenges. I don't think luck comes into it. Luck comes to the one who is prepared for it. So I took a long-haul approach. I don't think that one can 'plan' life, as things never turn out the way one thinks. One can have some broad strategy on which direction to take, but that is all. I have found that it is best not to look back.

By 1976 I had gained an HNC and a University Degree. By then I had a handful of good friends. I worked hard and I climbed the careers ladder. Every few years I made a jump to a higher position. But the workplace had long been changing. Big paternalistic companies have almost all disappeared. Everything is nowadays full of hard work and thoughts and emotional sweat. There is high unemployment and people are being made redundant daily... so what will happen to your lovely toys for which you worked so hard? And your family? So you work even harder.

And then one day I went to the boss and listened to all the praises about myself, but 'with regret, in the name of restructuring', I would have to leave. And that was that. My first days out of work felt like being released from prison. I looked up and saw beautiful blue sky and sunshine.

Again the temptation is to look back. Why me? What have I done wrong? But that is not my way. I enjoyed the newly found freedom and started to chart a new direction. I could survive without income for a year. I was over 50. So what? I started knowing myself through not simply writing but virtually crafting my CV. It took me one month of what seemed like endless rewrites. Contrary to advice I did not apply for hundreds of jobs but just targeted the ones I really wanted to do. And then the interviews... And then the rejection... And then five months later success.

A new job with new colleagues gave me many new challenges. Stress? Well to be quite honest I still bite my nails. And by the way, I did marry a lovely English lady and she does make for me excellent roast duck and cabbage and dumplings!

Healthy Man

> " *Go placidly amid the noise and haste* "

Max Ehrmann, 'Desiderata'

Objectives
- To develop a good strategy for your health
- To choose stress levels you are happy with

This chapter is important because
- Men's health is a subject that is relatively neglected
- Some stress and pressure may be healthy – when the level is right for you, you will feel OK
- You can choose how much stress you take on
- There are steps you can take when things get too much

Content
- Men's health on the agenda
- Your health audit
- Stress – a balancing act
- Making a fresh start

Men's health on the agenda

From the Men's Health Forum website: [1]

Why is men's health poor?

There are several explanations:

Many men are still brought up to believe that they must be strong and tough, and behave as if they are indestructible. This makes it hard for them to look after their health; in fact, it encourages risk-taking behaviours such as smoking, excessive drinking and dangerous driving. Having to be 'macho' also makes it harder to ask for help from a doctor.

Men have some in-built biological problems. The male sex hormone testosterone may raise the level of low-density lipoproteins (LDL), the 'bad' type of cholesterol that increases the risk of heart disease. Also, when men put on weight, fat tends to build up around the waist, the worst possible place in terms of developing the furred-up arteries that cause heart problems.

Because men don't have periods, they lack a mechanism that regularly and naturally makes them feel aware of, and in touch with, their bodies. What's more, men's reproductive systems don't require them to maintain any regular contact with healthcare services. They don't need to see a doctor to obtain contraception and, of course, they don't get pregnant.

Health services haven't done much to encourage men to look after their health. Most GP surgeries are still open only at times when men are likely to be at work, for example, and often don't feel like male-friendly places. There's also been chronic under-investment in research into male-specific problems, especially prostate disease.

Men, in general, have a shorter life expectancy and succumb to more preventable illnesses than women do. According to a leaflet published by the UK's Health Education Authority, this is not a chance of freak nature – it is because men do not look after themselves as well as they might, take bigger risks and are slower than women to respond to potential health concerns.

Whether this is because of ignorance, fear, isolation, apathy or bravado, the fact remains that men could be taking far more responsibility for their own (and other men's) health.

Men's lack of awareness and even interest in their health has serious consequences. For example, diseases affecting the prostate, an organ that is part of the reproductive cycle and only found in men, cause 6 times as many deaths as those from cervical cancer in women.

Men need to get their health into some perspective.

In this chapter you can do just that for yourself. To start with, take a moment to consider:

What might prevent you from paying more attention to your health?

Your body is your friend

Look on the bright side. Your body could be one of your best friends. After all, it is not a separate thing from you – just a vehicle, only there to carry your head around on. It is an integral part of yourself and you can benefit from having a good relationship with it.

And what a friend it is. Think about how amazing your body is:

- The heart of a man living 70 years will beat roughly 2 billion times. That's some reliable pump! It's even more amazing when you consider that more people than ever are living longer than 70 years.
- Think about your body's ability for repair – even serious wounds heal given time and the right conditions.
- There is a mysterious and important connection between your mind and your body. The way your body transforms food into energy is a chemical process, but availability of that energy relates to your state of mind. Therefore mental and physical health are closely related. Humans are complex beings, not simple machines.
- Medical science is more advanced than ever – there are cures for previously untreatable illnesses; even many cancers can be treated successfully if caught in time.
- Complementary therapies are increasingly available, which means that medicine is more wise than ever before.
- Bodybuilding and fitness aren't just the concerns of athletes

171

and film stars like Arnold Schwarzenegger. It is estimated that over half a million men in the UK regularly work out in a gym, and fitness is getting easier to achieve with the huge increase in accessible facilities.

So there is a lot to be optimistic about when it comes to fitness, but it takes a bit of effort on your part as well.

Healthy mind in a healthy body

If you are fit your body will deal with stress better and you may perform a better job, improving your chances of progress.

NASA has found that staff who exercise become more productive and work effectively for the full day, rather than just a part of it. This is part of a positive cycle:

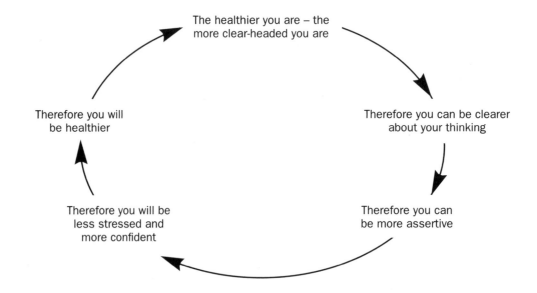

The healthier you are – the more clear-headed you are

Therefore you can be clearer about your thinking

Therefore you can be more assertive

Therefore you will be less stressed and more confident

Therefore you will be healthier

Of course there is the negative vicious cycle too, which you will certainly be able to figure out and avoid.

Your health audit

It's time to be honest with yourself. The golden rule of health and fitness is: *everything in moderation.*

Take a look at your health and fitness using this questionnaire:

Health history – a tale worth telling

As research shows that men tend to ignore or overlook their health, for a variety of reasons, you can do yourself a favour by thinking about your health history.

Have you had any major or minor operations or stays in hospital?

When?   What for?   What was the outcome?

Do you have any illnesses or conditions which seem to recur?
For instance, chest infections, skin conditions etc.

How often?   What are they?   How do you look after
                                                                                                yourself when they do?

What else can you think of that may be relevant in your health history?

Medical evidence also suggests that the physical make-up you inherit from your parents will play a big factor in your own health story. You will be most susceptible to illnesses and conditions that your parents, grandparents and ancestors had. Spend a bit of time finding out about or remembering the inherited physical make-up you have.

What is the general level of fitness you have inherited? How healthy were your ancestors?

What is the history of the following conditions in the men of your family?

 – *Cancer (smoking or non-smoking related)*

 – *Heart Disease (again with or without smoking)*

 – *Other diseases/conditions that you may or may not inherit the tendency for?*
    (such as asthma, eczema, etc.)

Diet – recipe for success

Do you eat a balanced diet – a variety of foods?

Never	Occasionally	Sometimes	Usually	Always
1	2	3	4	5

The balanced daily diet for the average man is:
- 2,500 calories per day
- No more than 20-30% fat (found in butter, marge, oil etc)
- 15% protein (found in fish, meat, beans etc)
- 60-70% carbohydrate (found in bread, pasta, potatoes, rice, etc, – remember chips have lots of fat!)
- At least 1 pound (500g) of fruit and vegetables – roughly five helpings

Most food is labelled on the packaging, giving the breakdown of these ingredients in them, so try counting up your totals for a week, eating your usual diet:

Day	1	2	3	4	5	6	7	Weekly total
Total amount eaten (grams)								
Total calories								
Fat (grams/ % of total)								
Protein (grams/ % of total)								
Carbohydrate (grams/ % of total)								
Fruit (grams/ % of total)								

How closely did you come to the ideal?

Nowhere near	Not very close	Some way to go	Quite close	On the spot
1	2	3	4	5

What do you want to change?

> ## TEN EXPERT TIPS FOR FIGHTING THE FLAB [2]
>
> 1. Exercise little and often
> 2. Limit fast food, processed and ready made meals
> 3. Turn your heating down
> 4. Wise up to food labels
> 5. Cut comfort eating
> 6. Don't be afraid to use slimming foods
> 7. Weight control is for life
> 8. Cook more often yourself
> 9. Weight control is a family affair
> 10. Eat smaller portions

Alcohol – name your poison

Most people will agree that you can have too much of a good thing. Alcohol is a good example of this. Doctors agree that a small amount of alcohol will actually do you some good – for men over 40 it can even reduce the risk of heart disease. But that means no more than 1 or 2 units – roughly one or two glasses of wine – a day at most. Men are advised that more than 3 or 4 units a day is unhealthy – that's about two pints of average strength beer. Some strong beers can have as much as 4 units of alcohol in a pint. Spirits are about 1 unit a shot.

If you drink to relax, bear in mind that above the recommended amount can actually have the opposite effect on your mood, making you more tense, aggressive or depressed.

What about you?

Take the last week into account. Include Friday and Saturday night as well as Monday or Tuesday.

How many units of alcohol did you drink this week?

Above 28 units	Nothing to be proud of
About 28 units	Still watch out
Between 14 and 28 units	Is that OK for you, or too much?
Between 7 and 14 units	Keep it that way
Less than 7 units	Not an issue for you

Was this a common or an unusual amount for you?

⌐ *What triggers you drinking the amount you do?*

⌐ *What do you want to do about this pattern?*

Smoking – kick the weed

There are people who smoke more than 20 a day and are still alive at 95. They can justify their habit that way. But the truth is that these people are the exception. If you do smoke, bear in mind that it isn't just the serious or fatal illnesses – heart and lung diseases – that you have to watch out for. Look at the everyday effects – like how long it takes you to get over a cold, or whether you can run up a flight of stairs without sounding like a steam engine.

Smoking is not good news for anyone, even if for some people it isn't all bad news. You should also bear in mind the history of smoking in your family. Did male smokers in previous generations contract diseases? How old were they when they did? This could have a bearing on your own likely outcomes.

> *Smoking-related diseases kill 40% of smokers before they reach retirement.*
> *The Complete Book of Men's Health* – Thorsons

The reality for most people who don't give up is that they want to smoke. If you don't really want to give up, you won't. Don't kid yourself. So what's the trade off that's really worth the risks?

⌐ *If you smoke, how many a day on average? Be honest:*

Above 40	This is a major issue for you to sort out
Between 20 and 40	A serious cause for concern
Between 10 and 20	What's your strategy?
Between 5 and 10	Re-assess the risks at regular intervals
Less than 5	Why not give up completely?

If you do, why do you smoke? Is it:

- – Just a habit?
- – Because other people around you do?
- – To help you relax?
- – Instead of eating?
- – All in the mind?
- – All in the body?

Other drugs   Also bear in mind other drugs that you consume and the risks they may hold for you.

What are they?
For instance, coffee, tea, and other prescribed drugs

Do you know what the maximum healthy limit is for these substances? If not, find out! How near are you to that maximum limit?

What are the long-term effects of these drugs on your health?

What do you want to change about your use of these drugs?

Physical activity – best foot forward   A general target for men, depending on age and experience, is between 30 minutes of moderate exercise, such as brisk walking or cycling, 5 times a week, and 20 minutes of more intense exercise, such as jogging or squash, 3 times a week. Any more than that and you will be getting pretty fit. Any less and there's room for improvement.

Bear in mind, according to the UK Men's Health Forum:
*61% of men in the UK consider themselves to be very or fairly fit.
Most of them aren't!*

How much physical exercise do you do in a week?

Less than 1 hour of moderate exercise	A big one to consider
Between 1.5 and 2.5 hours of moderate exercise	Stretch yourself a bit more
Up to 2.5 hours of moderate exercise	OK
Up to 60 minutes of intense exercise	Getting fit
Above 60 minutes of intense exercise	Getting very fit

NASA has found that staff who exercise become more productive and work effectively for the full day, whereas other workers' efficiency decreases by 50% in the last two hours of the working day.

Recognising the behaviour patterns

There are always positive actions you can take for your health, and you don't have to make the usual mistake of panicking about your health, entering into a strict regime of diet and exercise that would crush the spirit of an SAS recruit, which you only manage to keep up for a day and a half.

The best way to improve your health over the long-term is to recognise the bigger picture – how the patterns of behaviour and lifestyle you have contribute to your level of health.

For example, if you want to quit smoking, you might do better not going to the pub at lunch time but the swimming pool instead, where people around you are exercising rather than smoking. In that way, you will be changing the pattern of behaviour that prompts you to smoke. This is bound to be more effective than going to the pub and forcing yourself not to light up when everyone else does.

Similarly with your diet, if you want to eat less fat, then you may want to negotiate with your partner, if you have one, to do the weekly shopping and develop a new diet together, rather than trying to leave the chips at the side of your plate.

Looking at your lifestyle overall, and the health report you gave yourself, what behaviour patterns contribute to your health and fitness at the moment?

– *Behaviour patterns that encourage me to be healthy:*

– *Behaviour patterns that encourage me to be unhealthy:*

As a result of this, what action would you recommend yourself?

Summarising your health audit

It's time to take stock of all of this. Look back at the audit and write yourself a brief report, just as any doctor or health specialist might if they were given the same information. Ask yourself:

- What would they recommend?
- What would they say you were doing well with?
- What would they tell you to watch out for?

Write your own brief health report here:

10 TIPS FOR A HEALTHY PROSTATE [3]

1. Eat Essential fatty acids (EFAs) found in nuts, seeds and oils such as flaxseed oil
2. Take zinc
3. Eat pumpkin seeds
4. Take the herb, 'saw palmetto'
5. Take exercise
6. Consume selenium
7. Eat brassica vegetables (like Brussel sprouts, broccoli, cabbage and cauliflower)
8. Eat tomatoes
9. Eat oily fish (such as salmon, trout, mackerel, herring and sardines)
10. Drink soya milk

Stress – a balancing act

Home-to-work 'stress contagion' is worse for men than for women. That is, men's stressful home experiences are more likely than women's to spill over into their work, and affect it negatively. The stress 'biggies' for the guys are 'role overload' (feeling that their responsibilities in one area are making them less effective in another), arguments with their partners and arguments with their children. One of the reasons Parental Leave may be 'good for business' is that it may make men more adept at coping with home-stresses and at preventing 'stress contagion'. [4]

'Stress management' is a fashionable topic and there are many recommended strategies that you can explore in this chapter.

The best way of managing your stress and keeping it at acceptable levels is to:

**Be clear about what you really want in your life
and develop a strategy to achieve this.**

No amount of relaxation exercises or special diets will help you if you are not happy with your overall life situation. You need energy for what you do, to do it well and with the right levels of stress and pressure.

181

This means finding the right balance between:

- Time for yourself and time for others
- Work and leisure
- Family and friends
- Career and home life
- Pressure and relaxation
- Routine work and new projects

Everyone's point of balance for all these things will differ.

What are your 3 most important balances? Write them here:

1) The balance between _____ and _____
   At the moment, this balance is:

too far this way				too far this way
1	2	3	4	5

2) The balance between _____ and _____
   At the moment, this balance is:

too far this way				too far this way
1	2	3	4	5

3) The balance between _____ and _____
   At the moment, this balance is:

too far this way				too far this way
1	2	3	4	5

Healthy stress levels

Your stress levels will be about right when your important balances are on or near the middle; that is scoring 2-4 rather than 1 or 5.

A certain level of stress will be healthy for you. Distress may result when:

- You're doing the wrong things
- There isn't enough to do
- There's too much to do in the time available
- You regret not having been assertive
- What you have to do is too difficult
- Your 'head tape' tells you that you aren't doing well enough

Stress symptoms usually creep in unnoticed until you become ill or unhappy. The best way to manage them is to recognise them early.

What is the stress level in your life right now?

☐ Over the top, too much pressure
☐ A bit high, some pressure
☐ Comfortable, just right pressure
☐ Uncomfortable, too little pressure

What causes you stress now?

What are you already doing about it?

What do you foresee that may cause you stress in the near future?

How do you know when you're stressed? People know when they are stressed when they get ill or find themselves in distress, but what about your early warning signals?

Do you experience any of these?

One or two nights of not sleeping well	YES/NO	Forgetting things	YES/NO
Dropping things/clumsiness/accidents	YES/NO	Being irritable	YES/NO
Biting nails/grinding teeth etc.	YES/NO	Worrying	YES/NO
Wanting more time to yourself	YES/NO	Having aches and pains	YES/NO
Smoking/drinking/eating more	YES/NO	No energy	YES/NO
Taking unprescribed drugs	YES/NO	Feeling tense	YES/NO
Feeling frustrated/angry and then		Headaches	YES/NO
listless/down	YES/NO	Feeling sick	YES/NO

Add anything else that you know or think is a symptom of you being too stressed:

How many of these symptoms are you experiencing now?

Rather than worrying about these symptoms, consider the root causes of your stress. What choices can you make?

Most people know a lot about how to prevent their stress overload, but don't actually do anything about it to put their wisdom into practice.

What could you be doing more of or less of to get your stress levels back to where you want them?

The rest of this chapter gives you:

- Ideas about containing stress
- Hints and tips for short-term stress release
- An opportunity to start again

See Chapter 13 for Assertiveness, which can provide a strategy for dealing with stressful situations.

Making a fresh start

One simple way to alleviate stress is to try again to put into practice the things you know that will help. Rather than having the attitude that you have failed if you get stressed, develop the attitude that you can start again at every moment. And now is one of those moments.

Ask for what you need

It is said that men don't tend to ask for what they need. If you don't get what you need, you may get stressed. And if you don't ask, no one will know. So rather than inwardly boiling or feeling deflated, get into the habit of asking for what you need. This is a sign of strength.

Develop an unattached mind – letting go

If you wonder how some people seem so calm in the face of stressful situations, it is probably because they have removed themselves from the hustle and bustle around them, and developed a calm and detached viewpoint. They look at things from the 'bigger picture' point of view: 'What does this matter in the big scheme of things?' This is 'letting go'.

You can let go:

Physically: Try spending two minutes letting go of your body by tensing and releasing the muscles in your head, your face, your shoulders, arms, chest, stomach, legs and feet.

Emotionally: What feelings do you want to let go of? In what situations? Remember you are not just the result of your feelings. They will pass. You have choices about how you deal with them.

Mentally: Step back from your thoughts and observe them. Recognise the patterns your thinking goes through and say to yourself: 'This too will pass'. Remember the amount of time you have wasted worrying about events that never happened or didn't turn out the way you feared. Remind yourself of what you've got through before, and tell yourself you'll get through it again.

Try this technique in traffic jams. Tune out the world, tune in some tranquil music and forget about the appointment or whatever it is you're worried about missing. Worrying about it won't help you get there any quicker. Having a calm mind will help you do better when you do get there, even if you're late.

Medical and complementary health care

You deserve to be kept informed by anyone who gives you treatment. Ask lots of questions. Find out about what's on offer from your GP and what other treatments are available in your area. Medical research shows that people recover best when they are treated by a method in which they have confidence.

Pacing

Do you work in a job or undertake activities that have a pace that suit you or do you try and suit that pace? Find your niche with a pace that suits you. Say 'No' where necessary so you can work at your best pace.

Small steps and visionsAllies

Set smaller and more realistic targets in all things and give yourself real credit when you achieve them.

Find and work in with people who share your values and goals and who will support the changes you want to make in your lifestyle. See Chapter 5: Fellow Travellers – Your Supporters.

Have fun – laughter is the best medicine!

Other positive strategies

There are many stress-release products and techniques on the market. Find the one or two that suit you and use them. Local libraries and papers have lots of information about this. For example:

- Relaxation
- Massage/aromatherapy
- Yoga
- Tai Chi and other martial arts
- The Alexander technique
- Men's ritual groups
- Meditation and prayer
- Counselling/therapy

Note here any additional strategies you've tried or might like to try:

Overcoming nerves

There are also strategies you can develop that help you overcome nerves or stress in the short term. You can use them when things seem to pile on top of you, as an immediate stress reliever.

Here is one of them:

Breathing

Breathing is automatic – thankfully. But many people do not breathe as fully as they might. Calming your breath will calm your body and your thinking also.

Try this two-minute pause exercise:
– Sit upright and comfortable.
– Note the time.
– Close your eyes (or lower them to the ground if you don't want to appear to be asleep).
– Breathe through your nose, concentrating on breathing out all the air in your lungs, tightening your stomach muscles to push out all the air. This is better for you than just taking in a deep breath.
– Let your breath settle again and repeat the longer out-breath three times.
– Sit quietly just noticing the breath going in and out over your upper lip until you estimate that two minutes have passed.
– Open your eyes and check the time.

The first time you do this, two minutes may seem a long time, or it may have passed quickly. If you haven't ever done this before, it may seem strange or make you feel self-conscious. Keep trying. Practise it regularly and you'll get better at it, and it will become a good tool in your stress-relieving kit. You can use this exercise before interviews or other nerve-racking events.

Remember: breathe out.

Managing your stress-time

Think of all the time that is taken up with scattered thoughts and energy when you need to get on with something. Good time-management means good-quality thinking too. Here are three keys to manage your time in a way that manages your stress too:

Concentration – to sharpen up your ability to focus on a situation and give it your best attention
Planning ahead – to size up the situation
Containment – to keep stressful things under control

187

Concentration

Try this two minute concentration exercise on something totally unimportant. If you practise it regularly, you'll find your concentration on more important things improves greatly.

Two-minute concentration:

Take a very simple object that comes to hand, such as a pen, paper-clip or teaspoon. Concentrate on it for two minutes. For the two minutes think only about the object:

- What it is
- Where it came from
- What it looks like
- How it is made
- What it is made of
- What it is used for

When you find your mind wandering, bring it back to the object. Don't worry if at first you run out of thoughts before the two minutes are up.

Planning ahead

Planning can be substituted for worry. Having a plan and doing your preparation enables you to contain the worry. Feeling out of control of a situation is often a cause of undue stress. If you plan, then you will feel more in control. Make lists.

Often when you do start a plan, 'what ifs' may arise – thoughts about the consequences of what might happen, such as:

• What if the car breaks down?
• What if they ask me about budgeting?
• What if they say no?

Turn these 'what ifs' into a part of your plan.

Here's how. Think about one event in the future you are apprehensive about or getting over-stressed by. Pin down one of your 'what ifs' about the situation. Then put down what you will do if this does arise, so you have a strategy for dealing with it. Carry on until you have a plan for all your 'what ifs'.

Now you have your options ready and you can choose your best option, or leave it until the 'what if' arises. Very often, it won't.

┌
Situation:
What if…   *I will:*

Containment   Next time you find yourself worrying about something, remind yourself that you have already thought about it; that worrying won't really help and that you have a plan with all the 'what ifs' covered. Then tell yourself to stop thinking about it. Then stop!

Containment is a discipline – to choose what you will spend your energy thinking about and when you will think about it next. It works with practice.

And finally:

Me-time   In your me-time, you give yourself treats. When was the last time you felt you really did something just for yourself? It isn't self-indulgent, it gives you time to recover and re-energise. You can balance it with 'us-time' too, when you can choose to spend time with just the people you want to. Building in some time each day when you do just what you want to, or be with just who you want to be with, is a great de-stressor.

TAKE IT SERIOUSLY

- The average life expectancy of a male born in the UK in 1997 is still less than 75 years.

- Men who are defined as partly skilled or unskilled have a life expectancy of less than 70 years.

- The average man can expect to be seriously or chronically ill for 15 years of his life.

- The majority of men are too heavy for their health: 45% are medically defined as overweight and an additional 17% as obese.

- 28% of men still smoke.

- 27% of men drink alcohol at a level that could be harmful to their health.

- 41% of all male deaths under the age of 75 (almost 60,000 a year in the UK) are caused by circulatory diseases, the largest single cause of death. Of these deaths, over two-thirds (some 41,000) are due to coronary heart disease. Each year, over 130,000 men of all ages die from circulatory diseases.

- 31% of all male deaths under the age of 75 (almost 48,000 a year in the UK) are caused by cancer, the second most common cause of death. Each year, over 124,000 men of all ages are newly diagnosed with cancer and over 80,000 die.

- Prostate cancer is the most common cancer affecting men alone. Nearly 22,000 men in the UK are newly diagnosed with prostate cancer each year and about 9,500 die. The number of new cases diagnosed is expected to treble over the next 20 years.

- The suicide rate among men is increasing. The rate has doubled among 15–24-year-old-men in the past 25 years.

- Many men are affected by sexual problems. Recent American research suggests that almost one-third of men of all ages say they climax too early and nearly one-fifth of men in their 50s experience problems achieving or maintaining an erection.

But the news about men's health definitely isn't all bad:

- Men are more interested in their health than ever before. Increasing numbers of us are reading the health sections in men's magazines, surfing health web sites (you're reading this, after all!) and ringing the ever-growing number of helplines offering advice on impotence, prostate cancer or almost any other health problem affecting the modern male.

- Far fewer men now smoke – millions have already stubbed out just about the biggest single risk to their health – and they're also more likely to visit their GP than they were 25 years ago.

- Even the Government now accepts that action must be taken to improve men's health. Former public health minister Yvette Cooper MP said, on assuming her brief, that: 'One of the starkest health inequalities when it comes to life expectancy is that between men and women. The question for all of us who care about ill health among men is what we can do to make a difference.' [5]

Where do you want to go now?

Think about:
- adding to the notes section, where you can record any useful ideas in the blank pages at the end of the workbook
- deciding which chapter to go to next

Nigel – Yorkshire

Past
I lost interest in school and education, which is something I regret (although I have come to terms with this). My parents' divorce was too much of a negative influence.

Present
I feel lost, with no direction in my career, and changes at work which are making me wonder what I should be doing next. I need to change my priorities, find a new direction and make some decisions about my career.

Future
I hope our next cycle of fertility treatment is successful, and I will make sure our plans are in place so my wife and I can retire at 50.

Richard Montagu

– Stretching into self-employment

My first job was as a management trainee with a high-street chain store. Someone had said that they gave a good training and it was a good company to work with. I applied and they accepted me. I enjoyed the time I spent with them. It took me away from home for the first time in my life and taught me to think and plan in a clear, uncluttered way. However, I didn't make an effort and was bored.

A few jobs later found me drifting into an engineering company. This was the first occasion I really felt I had a mentor, an older man who was ready to give up his time to teach, guide and push me. I started to stretch myself. This was a marvellous opportunity to develop new skills. For example I had never before stood up before an audience and delivered a speech. The first occasion was terrifying. It has got better since!

I had decided that I wanted to take the step into self-employment. I knew that would mean stretching myself even more. This decision was reinforced in 1982, when my job with the UK end of a Swedish company was made redundant. I found this a difficult period. I knew it was the job and not me that was redundant, but it was still difficult to accept this. I had doubts about my ability. Luckily, I had a good friend, who pulled me out of my self-indulgence and showed me what a great opportunity this was. Now I could do what I wanted to do and be my own boss.

I have now been self-employed for sixteen years. I was told by a friend who was self-employed, that if I lasted two years, I would last forever. It is true. After the first couple of years, your friends and acquaintances can fall away. You are on your own then. You have to be good to survive. No one can overestimate the amount of determination you have to show.

I am now planning another career change. It all fits in well with what I do and what I am. It makes sense. I may well be about sixty by the time I qualify in this new area, but I will still have plenty of working years ahead of me, if that is what I want."

11

Feeling Good

" Emotionally intelligent people are self-directed self starters, highly
motivated and above all, excellent communicators. As such they
are likely to emerge at the top of organisations "

Dr. Daniel Goleman, *Emotional Intelligence*

Objective
- To be clear about how you feel, develop choices about how you express your feelings, and to use your feelings skilfully

This chapter is important because
- Men *do* know how to understand and express their feelings
- Being clear about how you feel makes you stronger and more powerful
- People respect those who can take responsibility for how they feel
- Knowing that there's a system to your feelings gives you self-sufficiency

Content
- Feelings have a point
- Feelings fitness
- Recognising your feelings
- Dealing with feelings successfully
- Paying attention to the feelings of others

Feelings have a point

Do men show as much empathy as women? Many people believe that men are not as 'empathic' (sympathetic and compassionate) as women. In fact, research shows that men are as capable of demonstrating empathy as women when they are motivated to do so.[1]

Feelings do have a point. They are an internal radar system, alerting you to dangers and possibilities. If you live out of touch with them, you miss out on an important tool, and take away a lot of the meaning of your life. Repressing feelings can also lead to mental and physical illness.

Since the 1990s there is a phrase for this approach – 'emotional intelligence'. Developed by former science journalist Daniel Goleman and described in a book of the same name... 'People around the world are facing the same problems' he says. What these difficulties come down to is that the so-called soft skills have become all-important, too long ignored or badly dealt with by organisations. Rather than, say, an ability to get the numbers right, these skills are now seen as the crucial factor in success... The ability to manage feelings, be a good listener and know who you are is not taught in school, but they can be learned.[2]

'Big boys don't cry' simply isn't true anymore. Not only big boys but adult men cry when they feel like it; they can be clear about and express a wide variety of feelings. This is all part of being a whole person in the modern age. During the Gulf War, for example, public opinion overwhelmingly supported the RAF pilots who returned from dangerous low-level raids in tears.

Film characters played by Stallone or Schwarzenegger can only express their anger by spraying bullets at innocent passers-by. 'I'll be back' may sound cool when the Terminator says it, but all he can do is return with guns blazing. Men successful in fields beside mass extermination can come up with a whole range of feelings, from sadness to fear to great joy and jubilation.

Being a feeling person means:

- Accepting the challenge to be an all round person
- Achieving more in your life

- Displaying strength by expressing your feelings in a wide range of ways
- Building better relationships

Getting clear about how you feel may sound risky – in fact it is far riskier for your health to not express feelings.

- Bottling feelings up can lead to health problems, such as ulcers
- Letting them out uncontrollably can lead to others, such as heart attacks

It doesn't mean:

- You must cry more or become unnecessarily touchy-feely
- You have to pretend to feel anything that you don't genuinely feel
- Being less 'manly'
- Being weak and vulnerable

Men express feelings their way. You have a unique emotional life, like all other men and women, and you can express how you feel your way.

I think men do express their emotions well. I do it myself, in my stand-up comedy act. I don't think it's true to say we don't express them. Men have feelings. I wouldn't be interested in another man's life if he didn't talk about it with feeling. We might have a laugh as well, but it is important to be serious sometimes. Men express feelings that way, differently to women.

David Baddiel – TV Presenter

Feelings fitness

Being aware of your feelings and choosing how you express them is a skill. It isn't a skill that most people get taught formally. But it is a skill that can be learned, just like other practical skills. You can use your feelings fitness just like your thinking intelligence, to solve problems and discover new opportunities for yourself and others.

The keyword of this skill is: appropriateness. There are appropriate ways of dealing with your feelings, depending upon where you are.

There are three ingredients of this skill of feelings fitness:

- Recognising your feelings

- Dealing with feelings successfully
- Paying attention to others' feelings

A key principle in this process of developing feelings fitness is:

**You may not be able to choose how you feel, but you
can choose how you deal with what you feel.**

Recognising your feelings

The first step in feelings fitness is to get into the habit of tuning in to what you are feeling and take ownership of this inner territory, which is your right.

Many people try to express how they feel by using the 'you' word, as in: 'If you have kids, then you have a responsibility towards them'. This isn't in fact a statement of feeling at all. It is in fact a statement of thinking. Compare this with using the 'I' word, as in: 'I feel a great sense of responsibility towards my children'. This is a true statement of feeling.

Using 'I' ensures that you:

- Don't make generalisations based on what you think you should feel
- Actually make a connection with how you really feel
- Speak for yourself and not others

If you breathe, you make a connection with your body, which is often where your feelings connect, and which acts as a channel for them. You can observe your feelings in your body – clenched teeth, a twitching foot, a rumble in the stomach.

What is your body telling you about your feelings right now?

Try and identify how you are feeling, starting with a breath, observing your body and using the word 'I':

'Right now, I am feeling ....'

You might have said:
annoyed – hungry – alert – inspired – irritated – content – confused – curious – bored – energised – sad – moved – tired, or none of these – a different feeling of your own.

There are so many different words to express how you feel. This shows how varied your feeling life is. The aim now is to make some sense of this range for yourself.

Your range of feelings

Feelings cover a wide range of sensations, emotions and sentiments.

Physical feelings: These feelings relate mostly to your body, such as hunger, tiredness and so on.

Emotions: These are your core curriculum of feelings, covered by the four basic categories of: joy, anger, fear and sadness. These relate to both your body and your state of mind. These four basic emotions are like the range of colours in a painter's palette; a mixture of blue and yellow gives green in the same way that a mixture of grief and anger gives despair, or joy and fear gives excitement or exhilaration.

States of mind: These are more to do with your attitude. They are the more complex human functions that give your life higher purpose, such as motivation and inspiration, and a sense of moral standards, such as guilt and responsibility.

Think of some feelings you have had during the past week. You can also add what you are feeling right now.

Whilst recalling these times, remember to:

* breathe and observe your body – it can remember sometimes better than your head
* use 'I'

For example:

* Walking to work: *'In this situation, I felt cold when I started out.'*
* At the dentist: *'In this situation, I felt scared it would hurt and then relieved that it didn't!'*
* Watching a film: *'In this situation, I felt very moved and inspired by the story.'*

Your examples:

A map of your feelings

Your feeling life is complex and you have a whole repertoire of feelings of many types.

Now you can make some order out of this, by mapping your feelings in this exercise. It will enable you to be clear about this important inner territory.

Using the three lists below, add the feelings that came up.

| **Body/**
external feelings | | **Mind/**
internal feelings |

	Physical feelings	**Emotions**	**States of mind**
e.g.	Cold	Angry	Responsible
	Tired	Sad	Guilty
	Sexy	Scared	Inspired
	Hungry	Happy	Ashamed
	....	....	....
	....	....	....
	....	....	....
	....	....	....
	....	....	....

You could also ask other people for their examples.

The chart on the next page is divided two ways:

- In a series of four concentric circles, for feelings you have often, sometimes, rarely and never
- In three segments, one each for sensations, emotions and sentiments

Write all your sensations, emotions and sentiments into the appropriate circle of the chart.

FEELINGS MAP

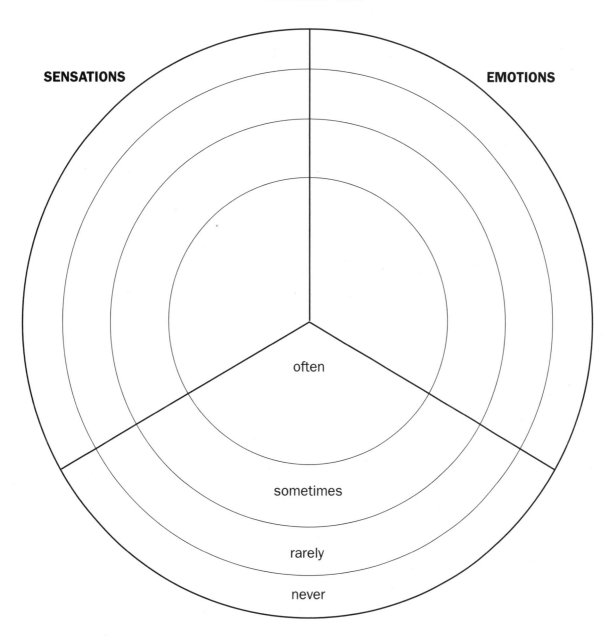

SENSATIONS

EMOTIONS

often

sometimes

rarely

never

SENTIMENTS

Arrange all the sensations in a pattern in the left segment, all the emotions in the right segment and all the sentiments in the bottom segment. Choose any pattern that makes sense to you, spacing them out across each circle and segment, using all the space in the diagram.

If you want to, write them using three coloured pens, for the different intensity you feel them:

Red   –   for very strongly felt

Orange   –   for quite strongly felt

Yellow   –   for not strongly felt

This chart is useful to give you a snapshot of your feeling life, which may change over time. Consider the following questions:

What, if any, surprises are there in your chart?

What areas of this map do you want to pay more attention to in future?

Dealing with feelings successfully

Being aware of how you feel is the first vital ingredient to feelings fitness. Once you are aware of your feelings, you can choose how you deal with them by:

- Expressing the feeling – letting it out
- Channelling the feeling into another activity
- Switching from one feeling into another
- Controlling the feeling for now
- Reasoning the feeling through

For example, if you are very angry about something, you might:

- Smash something, or shout
- Channel your anger into cool thinking
- Switch your anger into laughter
- Sit on your anger until it is safe to let it out, for example with a hard game of squash
- Reflect about whether it is worth getting so worked up about

Different choices of feeling will work best for you at different times. You can judge which will be the most useful in any particular setting. This judgement can be based on:

- What makes the circumstances better for yourself, others, or both, and not worse
- Channelling the feelings into the future instead of getting stuck in the past
- Ensuring that neither you nor anyone else gets hurt

- Doing something you will be proud of, not regret, later on
- Opening up new possibilities, being clearer about what you and other people can do next

For these five choices for dealing with feelings:

- Each has a constructive and destructive side
- None of these is necessarily better than any other
- It is best to be familiar with and skilled at all of them, rather than just one
- They can be used in any combination and are often best when used together

Recognising this range of responses to what you feel, and using them all if possible gives you a great deal of choice.

DEALING WITH FEELINGS: THE CHOICES

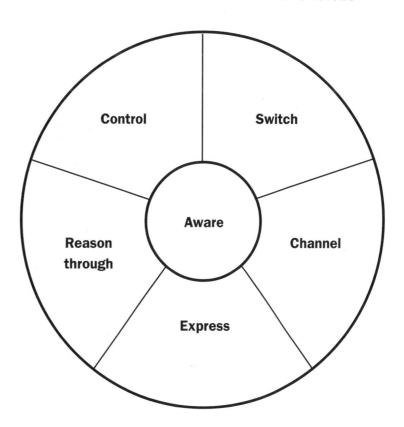

Expressing feelings This is where you let the feeling out. With a feeling such as anger, this might be where you act angrily, raising your voice, storming and so on. It can be constructive, in that it will be a release and other people will be clear about how you feel. It can be destructive because it may alienate people if it's directed at them, or even lead to violence. It may even become dangerous for your health.

201

Speaking your feelings

One way you can express how you feel is by simply telling others about it. There are advantages and disadvantages to letting other people know how you are feeling, and it depends on where you are. Being 'feelings fit' is also about being aware of the appropriateness of speaking about your feelings, or keeping them to yourself.

More often than not, because adults, and especially men, learn to hide their feelings, other people may have little indication of how you are feeling. But you have a choice: you can actually let them know. This may be very useful to both you and them, because:

- It will encourage them not to take how you are behaving personally, if they are not the cause of it
- It may make them more sympathetic, giving you the space you need to sort your feelings and thoughts out
- It may prevent you and others from digging yourself in deeper

Channelling feelings

This choice is about channelling your feelings into another activity. You may be more or less aware of doing so, but everybody has a feelings channel of some sort. Again, using the example of anger, it can be channelled into writing a very clear, cool-headed and assertive letter to someone, or putting up those shelves that you have been meaning to sort out for ages.

You might use the option to channel your feeling into an activity which deals constructively with the situation, and at the same time you are giving yourself more breathing space. Channelling your feelings into another activity could also enable you to discover a new area of creativity.

Art and music are good examples of where people channel their feelings into creativity. This can transform that feeling into something entirely new, perhaps as the inspiration for a new discovery.

As the Rastafarian poet, Benjamin Zephaniah says:

I had all this angry energy as a young man. I just needed to channel it. At first it led me into crime, but I could have become a car mechanic. In the end, I put this energy into my poems.

Some people find that sport is a good channel for their feelings. Many great boxers or footballers have been made from young men channelling their energy into their sport.

The constructive side of channelling feelings is that it can be very creative. The destructive side is that it can become an avoidance of your feelings if used too much.

Switching feelings

This is where you simply turn what you feel into another feeling and express that instead. A good example is how people laugh at sad occasions. This is because the grief they may be feeling simply switches into hilarity and laughter, sometimes because they know they are not supposed to be doing that. Similarly, some people will cry at very happy occasions. The emotion just switches from one thing to another. It is a perfectly natural response, an indication of the complexity of being human.

This can also have a very sinister side, for example, in how the feeling of jealousy can switch into anger and vengeance.

The most constructive side of switching is that it can enable you to express a feeling in a more comfortable way for yourself, like laughing when everything seems hopeless.

The destructive side of switching is that it can be inappropriate, for example, to laugh at someone's funeral.

Controlling feelings

Just as a deep breath and a moment's inward observation can get you in contact with your feelings, it can also be used to control them if things are getting out of hand.

Controlling feelings is something many children learn as they grow older. It is about choosing not to burst into tears if you have hurt your finger, but taking a deep breath and holding it in, until the situation has changed. You can go outside later and yell 'Ouch!' Or you may choose to delay expressing the feeling and channelling or switching it into something else. Everybody has different ways of controlling feelings.

Sometimes there are very positive reasons to control feelings:

- Letting them out, there and then, may just make things worse
- You can wait until it is safe to let them out
- It can demonstrate admirable self-control

Sometimes, controlling feelings can be destructive:

- It can become a way you cut yourself off from yourself and other people
- You may miss an opportunity to get some support
- If you control too much, it becomes avoidance

Avoidance warning signals

Many people are in the habit of avoiding how they feel, for a number of reasons:

- Because they were taught as a child 'not to be soft'
- Some of the feelings they have are very overwhelming
- A certain amount of avoidance is the only way they can get through very stressful situations

Avoidance is not always a bad thing, but too much avoidance means you are missing out on something valuable: a feeling life. Worse still, you may be doing yourself actual harm by constantly repressing what you feel. This doesn't mean that you should immediately get washed away by waves of emotion; more that you may benefit from being aware of and choosing how you express what you feel.

People avoid noticing how they feel through a number of mechanisms, such as:

- Explaining feelings away: 'Well, I would be angry about it, but what's the point?'
- Denying they have feelings: 'What? Me! Scared? Never!'
- Avoiding feelings altogether: ' Just leave it'
- Negatively judging their feelings. 'Oh I'm just being unreasonable. I should go away into a corner until I feel better.'
- Burying feelings through over-use of alcohol or drug dependency: 'I'll feel better after a few beers.'

Most people tend to use one or more of these methods at some time, especially in a world where fast-moving stresses and strains make it sensible to avoid feelings from time to time.

If avoidance goes too far it becomes repression, which has unhealthy physical and mental effects. Everybody has warning signals, internal alarm bells.

This warning might be:

- Getting ill more often than usual
- Getting drunk or stoned very often
- Having a lack of energy
- Having relationships that don't seem to work out
- Thinking you can cope and then making mistakes
- Feeling isolated
- Wondering why your life seems so pointless

Your examples:

What action could you take to respond to the warning?

Reasoning feelings through

This is about using your powers of rational thought. It is about thinking things through, so the feelings are no longer appropriate or are changed. It requires that you look at the bigger picture. It may be that you find something out that shows the feeling isn't justified. You could ask important questions about the circumstances of your feelings, so that they change.

With grief over a death, for example, it might be that the person you are grieving for would not want you to be unhappy. Although it is hard, you might be able to convince yourself that they were right and that might ease your grieving process. With anger, it may be that the person you are angry with did not mean to be hurtful, and you can find that out by asking them some questions. This new information may dispel your rage.

You are capable of the great power of rational thought, and using this with your feelings will enable you to manage your life more effectively.

A constructive side of reasoning feelings through may be that it stops you rushing in and making a mistake you will regret later on. It may save you expending unnecessary energy on something, and may give you new options.

A destructive side of reasoning things through is that if you do it all the time, it can become oppressive to yourself and others, as it may stop you from feeling and that would be isolating.

Balancing the five choices

Tick how you're doing:

I need to:	MORE	ABOUT RIGHT	LESS
Express feelings			
Channel feelings			
Switch from one feeling to another			
Control feeling for now			
Reason feelings through			

Taking time – setting long-term feelings goals

You have developed your feeling life over the course of your whole lifetime. It is unreasonable to suggest that you can change how you deal with your feelings overnight. Give yourself some time with your feelings goals.

The first step is to clearly identify your feelings. Then you can decide if there are any changes you can make in how you deal with them. It may be that at first you just decide on one feelings goal and aim for that.

Peter Baker and Mick Cooper, authors of *'The MANual'*, suggest the following steps towards setting long-term feelings goals, which build on the ideas in this section:

- Keep a diary – try to explore what prompts particular feelings
- Change the way you talk – use 'I' rather than 'you', 'one' or 'they'
- Reflect on your feelings regularly
- Spend time with people who accept your emotions
- Write an open letter – to a friend, a partner or even yourself. You don't have to send it
- Try to let go more. It may even mean bursting into tears when you are watching Oprah. Little by little, see how emotionally expressive you can be

Having read through the previous pages, what long-term feelings goals are you going to set?
For instance, I am going to talk to my friend about how upset I still feel about the death of my father.

Paying attention to the feelings of others

The more aware you are of your own feelings, the more you can tune in to the feelings of others, which will enable you to understand them better. There are also important links between feelings and assertiveness, because three crucial elements in assertiveness are: listening to others, demonstrating you understand them, and being able to say clearly what you think and feel.

You will be looking more closely at listening and assertiveness in Chapter 13.

For now, you can consider briefly how much attention you pay to the feelings of others. How often do you ask yourself in a particular situation 'How does anyone else feel right now?' How might this be affecting how they are behaving? If you are more aware of your own feelings and how you behave when you have strong feelings, you have more ideas on which to base your insights into other people.

What is important is to separate in your own mind:

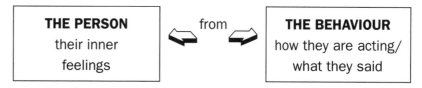

THE PERSON their inner feelings	from	THE BEHAVIOUR how they are acting/ what they said

Where someone is behaving very angrily, you can practise separating their angry behaviour from the person inside, who may be going through many things. Then you can respond to how they are behaving rather than reacting to them as a person.

Over the next day, keep a log of how other people demonstrated their feelings:

How did they or others act?

What did they say?

How do you think they were feeling?

What evidence or hunch do you have for this?

Dealing with different feelings in others

Very often, the feelings you are less familiar with will be your biggest challenge when someone else is feeling them. This may affect how you respond to them.

Looking back to your Feelings Map on page 199 which feelings do you feel least often?

How do you tend to respond when others are expressing these feelings?

Bear these feelings in mind and develop a strategy for dealing with other people.

For example, if you find anger quite difficult to tune in to and express yourself, you might want to develop a strategy for dealing with angry behaviour in others. This might be to focus on

separating their behaviour from who they are, and practise
assertively standing your own ground.

What strategy can you adopt?

Group feelings

Human beings are group animals. We have evolved in a social
setting so we are greatly influenced by one another. It might be
that many people are feeling the same thing. You might be caught
up in that wave, unless you are clear about what you feel.

A good example of this is a football crowd, where the supporters
seem to develop a group feeling they all share. This can of course
be very enjoyable and comforting if you are just watching football
or a rock concert perhaps, but the same process can be used
towards less innocent ends, such as at a political mass rally,
where the charismatic speaker can influence great numbers of
people towards a dangerous end, by whipping up people's
emotions. Adolf Hitler did this at famous mass rallies before World
War Two.

Of course, group feelings aren't only around at mass rallies – they
are also present in even the smallest group of people, in an office
or home. It is important, then, to be clear about the way group
feelings can affect you.

In what situations, and how, are you influenced by group feelings?

What do you want to change about this?

It isn't necessarily a bad thing to be swept away by the mood of the crowd. But, as with everything else in the realm of feelings, it is very useful to be aware of how you are affected and what you are feeling. Then you can choose how you respond. You are entitled to your feelings.

Where do you want to go now?

Think about:
- adding to the notes section, where you can record any useful ideas in the blank pages at the end of the workbook
- deciding which chapter to go to next

Peter – Essex

Past

I see myself as a survivor – a survivor of school, indifferent health, two serious road accidents, a major industrial explosion, a tyrannical boss, a move to Essex, and two marriages. I am bruised and battered, scarred and scared, but I am still alive.

Present

Life is full and empty at one and the same time – full of activity but empty of purpose. I am a single parent – the parent part I love but the single part I hate.

Future

My intention for the future is to take better care of myself and those around me. To misquote an old song, I see it is as both 'What you do and the way you do it'.

Good Thinking

" *My concern has always been with human thinking because this seems to me to play a central role in human happiness* *"*

Edward de Bono

Objective
- To explore the way you think and the tools you can use to become more effective

This chapter is important because
- The way you think has a powerful effect on your development
- Positive thinking is a skill you can develop to give yourself many more options

Content
- What you think and how you think
- Positive thinking
- Intuition – the sixth sense
- Your creativity

What you think and how you think

> *It is not what you think but how you think that really matters.*
>
> Johan Quanjer – *The Luminous Journey*

In Chapter 3, you looked at what you think, that is your values, attitudes and beliefs and how they affect your life. In this chapter, you pay attention to how you think, that is, how you can use a wide range of thinking tools. Being clear about how your thinking operates alongside your feelings will expand your range of options.

Thinking is like air: it's all around and vital for life, but because it's invisible you might not consider how important it is, until its quality becomes poor.

Much of your thinking pattern has been laid down from the very early years of life. You were taught to think in a certain way, by the people who have had an influence on you, such as:

- Parents – or whoever brought you up
- Teachers
- Friends
- Partners
- Colleagues and work-mates

All these influences have had an impact on your thinking, just as you will have affected theirs.

As with attitudes and values, these ways of thinking may also have been influential because of your rebellion against them.

There is also the influence of the society around you, which has particular ways of thinking, as seen in the media, the newspapers and television, which reflect all the various and diverse viewpoints of society. The way people think is also expressed in the laws of the land, both in how they are applied and what they actually are. You can see how the thinking of countries differs in their different political and legal systems. Of course, that is not to say everybody in a country thinks the same way. It just gives us a picture of commonly held patterns of thinking.

What or who do you think have been the biggest influences on the way you think?

How much does your thinking affect the people around you?

Positive thinking

> *All we are is the result of what we have thought.*
>
> Buddha

Thinking is a skill. How you think is about using a tool box, your mind and your brain, in a certain way. With a tool box, certain tools are best for certain jobs. You wouldn't get very far trying to change a fuse in a plug with a spanner. Positive thinking is about the general condition of your tool kit, how sharp your knife is and how secure the handle is on your hammer.

Being positive in your thinking will provide a way for you to see new opportunities, rather than getting stuck in old patterns and rigid ways of thinking.

It is a flexible system, because as well as being useful for big issues, it can also be helpful for anybody in the routine activities of daily life.

De Bono says there are **five principles to the 'positive revolution'** as he calls it:[1]

1. **Being effective** – Paying attention to the purpose of your thinking: asking 'Why do I think that way?'
2. **Being constructive** – Always looking for a way forward: for solutions, not problems
3. **Being respectful** – Having respect for others and for the effect your thinking has on them
4. **Self-improvement** – This is your right and duty to make more of yourself through your thinking
5. **Contributing** – Being more aware of what you can give than what you can get

213

Six Thinking Hats™   The six hats[2] method of parallel thinking was designed by Edward de Bono and is now widely used around the world as an improvement on argument. There are six hats of different colours which represent different ways of applying thought. You can wear these hats in any order you choose, to develop new ideas and solutions.

Like a hat, other people may be able to see it on you better than you can sometimes. Good feedback may be required to point out what type of thinking you are applying. And you can do the same for others, pointing it out if they only tend to wear a limited variety of thinking hats.

These hats are:

Blue hat: the hat that organises the others. With the blue hat you set the focus, summarise and conclude.

White hat: What we know, what we want to know, and how we will find out.

Red hat: the hat of feelings, emotions and intuitions. The red hat wearer can put forward his direct feelings on the subject without any justification; this is instinct, the raw 'gut reaction'.

Black hat: the hat of caution. With the black hat, you make a judgement about the problems.

Yellow hat: the hat of optimism, the positive hat.

Green hat: the hat of creativity. New green shoots of growth, ideas, spontaneous alternatives and new concepts strike the wearer of the green hat.

How good are you at:

Blue – organising your thinking?

Do it too much		About right		Could do it much more
1	2	3	4	5

White – Gathering all the relevant information and thinking about what is missing?

Do it too much		About right		Could do it much more
1	2	3	4	5

Red – Using your intuition, feelings and instinct?

Do it too much		About right		Could do it much more
1	2	3	4	5

Black – Being cautious – looking for the problems?

Do it too much		About right		Could do it much more
1	2	3	4	5

Yellow – Being optimistic – looking for the opportunities?

Do it too much		About right		Could do it much more
1	2	3	4	5

Green – Being creative – generating new concepts?

Do it too much		About right		Could do it much more
1	2	3	4	5

Which hat do you feel most comfortable in?

Which one is most alien to you?

Think of a current problem or decision in your life, either at work or at home. Using your 'white hat' write down the bare facts, the observed data in this setting, as you see it. Try not to 'think' about it, just decide what it is and apply your 'white hat', gather the information about it – the plain 'nuts and bolts'.

It could be:
- 'I have to buy a new car – which one should I choose?'
- 'My partner wants to have another child and I'm not so sure.'
- 'I don't quite see a way forward in my job.'
- 'What further education course should I choose?'

Write yours here:

Now apply the six hats system of thinking to your decision:

Hat used: Thinking:

_____   _____

_____   _____

_____   _____

_____   _____

_____   _____

_____   _____

_____   _____

_____   _____

_____   _____

Which hats did you use most?

Which hats were harder for you to use?

Which hats were the most useful in this situation?

In future, which hats do you think would be helpful for you to wear more often?

In order to think creatively:
- *Be foolish*
- *Expect the unexpected*
- *Break the rules*
- *Ask 'What if...?' questions*
- *Make mistakes*
- *Follow your intuition*
- *Take risks*
- *See the bigger picture.*

Roger von Oech

On the next page is an example of a creative thinking tool. A group of Navigator participants have used a diagram to describe their experience of being on the Navigator programme.

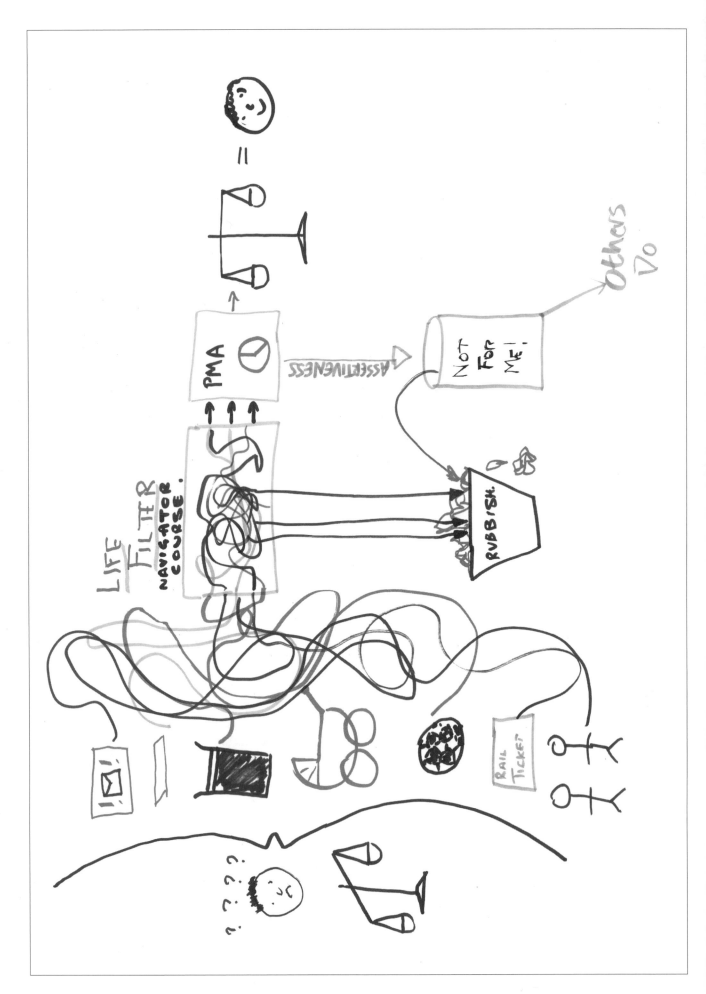

Intuition – the sixth sense

Think about how you find out about the world around you. Is it just through what you see, hear, taste, smell or touch – in other words your five senses? Or is there another 'sixth sense' at play? If so, how does it work?

If you cannot know exactly what may happen in future, how can you make any decisions about what to plan for? You need to develop a sixth sense, a gut feeling or hunch about what may be happening in your life and the world around you. This sixth sense can also be called 'intuition'. Intuition means 'immediate insight'; it suggests that there is something inside you that can tune in to the less obvious but important patterns of life. Intuition is another important tool in your thinking kit-bag. And it is a tool that you can sharpen with some insight and practice.

In the old war films, the general, often played by John Wayne for example, would say, 'It's quiet – too damn quiet! They're up to something!' In this case, the man was using his intuition.

Intuition is not hocus pocus – it is a serious business. In a survey of 20 top politicians and business people, 10% of mistakes made were attributed to 'not acting on intuition'. This was particularly related to hesitating whilst someone else took advantage of a business opportunity.[3]

However it works, intuition is an increasingly precious commodity in a world which is changing so fast that the information we get from our other five senses is not enough to make good and clear decisions.

A television producer, working in live news broadcasts, put it this way:

Working in live TV, you always know the things you need to know to make a decision, the moment after you needed to know them! In other words, we are always looking at an incomplete picture of what is going on, and if we waited for the complete picture, it would be too late. Therefore, we need to decide what to do using our intuition as readily as our eyes and ears.

Developing intuition is really a skill of tuning in to the bigger picture of what is going on both around and within yourself. It is a very old skill – it has been around as long as human beings have needed to avoid danger and seek out new opportunities.

You have intuition, whether you are aware of it or not. You may use it at certain times more than others. Some people feel more intuitive when they are relaxed and not feeling too stressed within themselves. Others develop acute intuition only when they are under extreme pressure. When is your sixth sense at its peak of power? The more widely you use it, the better it will be for you.

You may be tuned in more to what is going on or what might be about to happen:

- When you are driving on the motorway
- When the Cup Final is on
- When your child may be in danger
- When buying a house
- Depending on the weather
- When totally relaxed and at peace with the world
- When dreaming

In what other situations might your 'sixth sense' of intuition be at work? Use the next activity to have a closer look at your own intuition.

Noticing your intuition Over the next few days, make a note of some times when you felt your intuition was active. Try to find a range of different environments, in the office, street, bus, home and more.

Describe exactly what happened. Who did what?

How were you aware of your intuition?

Have there been times when you never/rarely felt intuitive? What were they?

What did you do as a consequence?

Why do you think it is hard for you to feel intuitive in this situation? What blocks your intuition?

What can you do more of in the future to develop your intuition?

Your creativity

> Imagination is more important than knowledge.
>
> Albert Einstein

How you use your creativity is another important part of the way you think. Everybody has a creative side to themselves. This does not mean that we are all a Michelangelo, but with most people, the fact that they are not a great artist, poet or similar means that they tend to deny the fact that their own creative, imaginative side exists at all.

This is a great pity – because using that creative side is an important skill when it comes to dealing with everyday life.

221

Left-brain and right-brain thinking

The human brain is physically divided into two halves, which are linked by a complicated nerve system. Measuring brain activity has shown that these two halves tend to specialise in different activities. The left side of the brain in most people, especially in western countries like the UK, tends to be more active for logical thinking, involving language, numbers, reasoning things through, the control of limbs of the body and so on. This is why more than 70% of the population tend to be right-handed, because the left side of the brain is more dominant over the right side of the body and vice versa, due to the curious cross-wiring of the human anatomy!

At the same time, the right side of the brain tends to be more active in imaginative activities, such as drawing, music and painting, and the understanding of how things fit together.

Western culture tends to value logical, rational thought more than creative, imaginative thought, especially when it comes to thinking at work. This situation is changing, because it is now more generally realised that imagination and originality will often provide solutions where logic and reason just bog you down.

At NASA, during the 'Apollo 13' emergency in 1970, the three astronauts were in great danger when an explosion disabled their spacecraft. Their air supply was low and they didn't have enough purification filters to clean up the air for their emergency return journey. No matter how much the scientists at Mission Control tried to measure it, there was only enough air for two days and the astronauts needed four.

Then one of them realised that they had spare filters left over from the now useless other space capsule, which didn't fit into the rescue ship's air system. The chief mission controller put a group of people in a room with all the things that the astronauts might have lying around in their rescue ship; anything from spare space suits to sticky tape and plastic bags, and using sheer ingenuity, the group came up with a Heath-Robinson system that worked. The astronauts were saved by the pure, creative imagination of those people on the ground.

In this example, the group in the room had to switch from using their left-brained, number-based thinking to more creative, imaginative, right-brained thinking, in order to come up with a solution to the crisis. For the sake of those three astronauts, it worked.

Right-brain thinking is about using the green, red and blue hats in Edward de Bono's system. Left-brain thinking is about using the white, black and yellow hats.

So, to summarise:

Left-brain functions	Right-brain functions
Right side of body	Left side of body
Used for logical thinking	Used for imaginative activities
Facts	Drawing
Language	Music
Numbers	Painting
Reasoning things through	Understanding how things fit together
Control of limbs	Intuition
Analysis	Ideas
One thing at a time	Multi-tasking

There is no straightforward division between left-brain and right-brain functions: because the brain is such a complex organ, nobody really yet knows exactly how it works. It just seems that with most people, the brain is active in this particular way.

The important question for you to consider is:
In a world that increasingly values right-brain skills as well as good old left-brain skills, how capable are you of switching from one to the other and back again? How much of a risk is this?

Your right-brain activity

Have a go at a right-brain activity to focus your thinking on something in your life right now.

This activity could focus on:

- A current problem or decision
- How you are feeling right now
- What you are thinking right now
- Where you think the opportunities for you are in future
- What are your greatest skills and talents
- Who the people are that you care about
- What your hopes, dreams and fears for the world are

Using all or any of these themes, or another one of your own choosing, try an activity which will enable you to practise your right-brain skills.

You could:

- Draw a picture using lots of colour, shapes etc.
- Write a story or poem
- Keep a creative diary
- Sing a song or whistle a tune
- Cut up pictures and words from the Sunday papers to make a collage
- Chose ten pieces of music that tell your life story and explain why they fit together
- Buy or make a special piece of clothing and wear it to a party
- Commentate on your life as if it were a football match
- Go dancing
- Pretend you are the central character in a movie or play and write a brief script
- Build an object of clay, plasticine or toy bricks
- Try drawing using your left hand if you are right-handed or vice versa
- Build or make something you can use

Points to note:

- This is for you – no one else need judge it or even see it if you don't want them to – they might not fully understand it and that is not important to you
- Give yourself a good and regular amount of time, say an afternoon or a couple of hours at least, every couple of weeks or more if you like
- Find a private, quiet space that would best suit the activity you choose, for example, a big flat work desk if you choose to paint a picture
- Make sure you've got all the resources you need, lots of large sheets of paper, paints, pastels, (the more colours the better) scissors etc.
- Persist! Don't give up at the first attempt

The most important ingredients of a right-brain activity are:

- Any creative materials that appeal to you
- Some time and space
- Imagination
- An open, enquiring and observant attitude

These are just a few of the right-brain activities for you to choose.

You could also try the following:

The quest   Go for a walk for an hour, somewhere beautiful or relaxing, where you can just reflect quietly to yourself and as your journey progresses, pick up five objects (not stealing anything of course!) and bring them home with you. They could be any five objects, stones, sticks, leaves, paper etc. and you may not know immediately why you were attracted to picking them up; they just seemed to 'call out' to you.

- Be very choosy
- Only choose objects you can easily carry

When you get back, lay them out in front of you and start to explain to yourself, either in words or using a picture, why these objects are symbolic of your life right now.

Consider:

- What are the links between them?
- What are their special qualities?
- What stories do they tell?
- What are the reasons they might be significant?
- What new insights does all this give you in your current situation?

You can always repeat this exercise – many men have had the powerful experience that it is a very good way of gaining right brain insights into the direction their lives are taking.

What was the most useful thing about doing this activity?

What was most challenging about it?

Where can you apply more right brain thinking in future?

> *Discovery consists of looking at the same thing as everyone else and thinking something different.*
>
> Albert Saint George – Nobel Prize Winner

Where do you want to go now?

Think about:
- adding to the notes section, where you can record any useful ideas in the blank pages at the end of the workbook
- deciding which chapter to go to next

Graham – Tunbridge Wells

Past

Hang on a minute – haven't I been here before? This bright happy atmosphere full of laughter and fun. A village called East Peckham, a small quiet boy, not a lad, but just true.

Present

It's a long way from where I am now, although some may not agree. I still have my school bag, my lunch box, but can now hold my pee. I am still having fun, and enjoy all types of fun, although perhaps not so good at all that I do.

Future

So where is tomorrow? I've heard it never comes. I'll still be at Highbury, cheering for my life. If people remember the ginger called Graham, I want them to say, 'He's not too bad, he was OK!'

Getting Yourself Across

> **"** *I am not suggesting that you should necessarily change the way you speak, but it is essential to be aware of the impression you are giving.* **"**
>
> Diana Mather – *Image Works for Men*

Objectives
- To be clear about the messages you want to give about yourself
- To look at the most effective ways of putting that message across

This chapter is important because
- Good performance is not enough – it has to be sold and noticed
- Impressions count
- Communication is a skill which needs thought and practice

Content
- Getting yourself across
- Why manage your image?
- Your visibility
- The image/message link
- Assertiveness
- Assertiveness in practice
- Meaningful mission statement

Getting yourself across

Are you getting yourself across in the way you want? Everyone creates an impression by how they come across to others. Even if you choose not to create an impression, you still create an impression by:

- The message you give out
- The image that goes with the message
- The words, voice, appearance that you have
- How visible you are

In this chapter, explore how you're getting across to others and check out your assertiveness.

Image works

What is the right image and why is it important? We all have an idea of how we project ourselves, but how many of us stand back and analyse the impression we convey to others? When we meet someone for the first time, ninety per cent of our opinion of that person will be formed within the first twenty to thirty seconds. If we want to project the right image, then, we do not have much time to waste.

Diana Mather – *Image Works for Men*

Why manage your image?

As you saw in Chapter 7, the factors that determine whether someone got promoted or not are:

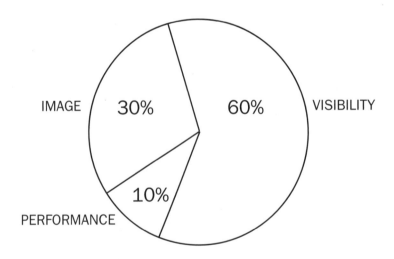

Although it may not sound fair, it is quite understandable that the image someone gives and the exposure they get counts for so much. Most people these days are overloaded with information to process, about every subject and in every aspect of life. This means that they generally won't have the time or energy to pay attention to your achievements, unless you tell them. If you think about it, you are probably the same about what other people are up to. How do you notice them unless they actively draw your attention?

This goes for all aspects of your development. Unless you tell them, how will people know:

- You're doing a good job
- What matters to you
- That you want to make a change or get promoted
- That you exist
- What other skills and capabilities you offer
- That you're ready for more training
- That there's more to you than what you do at work

Being good at what you do still counts for a great deal, but as well as this you have to broadcast your achievements and abilities in a way that fits in with your values and your image of yourself, and your visibility – that is, how well known you are. You will have to take the initiative here, and tell people about you, because they won't ask.

A good image lets people see your good performance

Most people feel better about themselves when their good performance is recognised, but recognition only comes when other people can see how well you are doing. You can put this across through your image. Your image needs to genuinely reflect your achievements and aspirations.

For some, the idea of building an image seems to suggest that you become phoney, superficial or even manipulative.

Others believe that if you explain too well about your achievements, it will ruin your chances of getting on because you will be seen as too valuable where you are.

These are unhelpful views, are negative 'mind viruses' around you which can sabotage your own development. You will benefit from a realistic and positive image of yourself and, as the statistics show, this will help you to move on in the vast majority of cases. If you haven't been doing this, it may explain why:

- Others seem to get jobs for which you are well qualified

- No one takes your idea of setting up your own business seriously
- Your ideas get ignored
- You get taken for granted

Your image is always with you, like a shadow. Even if you choose to ignore it, others will notice it; they will still form an impression of you. But you aren't stuck with your image like you are stuck with a shadow. You can change and adjust it.

Image is about the whole impression you give of yourself. A good image is a balance between two extremes:

So concerned with image
that you lose your real self

No concessions
to image

Image to fit your values
and your goals

- At one end of the scale is the person who pays so much attention to his image that he loses any credibility for his skills and achievements. He's a phoney.
- At the other end is someone who does not consider image important and expects that performance alone will gain him the recognition he'd like. He's likely to get ignored.
- In the middle is the person who has an image which fittingly puts across his values, his identity and his goals.

Your visibility No, visibility isn't about becoming a 'Chippendale' and stripping off! It's about the level of your profile – how noticeable you are. Remember Harvey Coleman's statistics: visibility contributes 60% to promotion. That means it is vital.

Visibility is about:

- Getting yourself known
- Getting your name known
- Getting your face known
- Getting your achievements and aspirations known

Some ways of doing this are:

- Extending your network of contacts
- Reminding people you still exist and telling them what you are up to now
- Getting involved in other activities, such as sports or other social events
- Organising things
- Writing articles
- Getting yourself in the local newsletter/paper
- Speaking up at meetings and on courses
- Being memorable – for whatever reason
- Having a card printed with your contact details/skills and qualifications
- Volunteering for things

There is a saying: 'There is no such thing as bad publicity'. This might not be entirely true, because once you have got a reputation it can be hard to change it. But there may be some truth in the idea that it is better for people to remember you for anything than not being remembered at all.

Be memorable

You are a unique individual. The trouble is, so is everyone else. Having some kind of technique or strategy to make yourself memorable can work wonders, and can give you the chance to put across your uniqueness.

For example, when Michael Grade, Chair of the the Governors of the BBC, was working his way up the TV networks in America, he was told that he needed to do something that would make him stand out. He decided to wear red socks. From then on, he always wore them and they became his trademark.

Of course there are many other ways you can be memorable, ways in which you can show that you:

- Stand out
- Are convincingly different
- Are a risk-taker
- Deserve special respect
- Renew your image
- Are preferable to the competition

231

Think of one thing about yourself that makes you memorable:

Mobility and putting yourself out

When you are promoting yourself, you can consider how far you are prepared to move house or travel to accommodate the needs of others.

If you are able and prepared to move about anywhere at any time, that can make you special, so it is worth making it clear in your image. You can decide how far it is worth going for a potential client or employer.

'Putting yourself out', making that special effort cheerfully every now and again, will also be a way in which you can make yourself memorable. It is something of course that you need to balance with the other aspects of your life.

You can put yourself out for your partner, your children or the local community too.

Putting yourself out is part of your public relations campaign. When a shop has a special offer, they make sure you know about it. You need to do the same. You also have to make sure that they have noticed you have done so, without going over the top about it.

Some ways of demonstrating what good value for money you are and how you are prepared to put yourself out are:

- If your organisation offers it, get a secondment or attachment to another department – they could become a potential new employer one day
- Volunteer to do things
- Get involved in working parties or steering groups
- Organise social events
- Have bright ideas and tell people about them

Don't let this mean that you do too much for nothing. The shop that offers a freebie keeps an eye on its 'profit margin' all the same. So should you.

Other public relations exercises

Most people buy goods, especially more expensive ones, on the recommendation of someone else. This is the same for your own PR campaign. If someone says you're great, that is bound to carry more weight and credibility than if you do. Be prepared to use formal referees as well as less formal recommendations, where someone else drops your name into a conversation.

PR is an ongoing process. Make sure that you keep people informed of new developments in your life, your skills and your abilities.

The image/message link

Research by Professor Albert Mehrabian[1] shows that the ways people receive messages from you will fall into three categories:

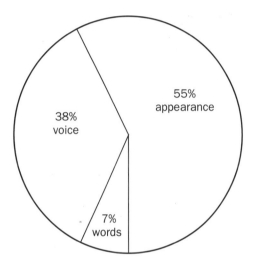

More than half the impression you create with others comes from how you look. This is something most people are aware of, for example when they go to interviews. However, this effect continues all the time, so you need to offer a consistent message in your appearance in order for it to be really effective.

The first things we notice about another person are their gender and race. If you think about what forms the rest of your first impression of someone else, several factors will probably come to mind:

- Their clothes
- Their handshake
- Their posture – how they carry themselves
- How fit and well they look
- Whether they look you in the eye
- The expression on their face
- Their hair
- Their jewellery

233

- Their mannerisms
- The opinions they express

So it's not enough to wear the right clothes – you have to wear them well and express the image you want. Think about your image alongside your values, identity and goals – do they match?

Write below some specific ways relating to these factors in which your message can be put across: For instance, the message I want to put across is that I'm friendly, so I smile at people.

You never get a second chance to make a first impression, so remember to:

- *Choose clothes suitable for the occasion*
- *Stand tall when you enter a room*
- *Look the other person in the eye*
- *Give a firm handshake*
- *Know what you are going to say*

Diana Mather – *Image Works for Men*

The handshake

A lot can be said about this gesture which is universally used as a greeting in western culture. Generally speaking, offering an open palm facing up demonstrates openness or even submission, and a palm facing down demonstrates caution and even a move to take control. Offering the hand straight out, palm vertically is more likely to be met equally by the other person.

Also the strength of the handshake will communicate much. People will appreciate a handshake which neither crunches their bones nor feels like a wet fish. There are other factors as well, such as whether the other hand is also moved forward during the shake, to 'glove' the hands, or hold the upper arm or shoulder, which can demonstrate anything from a trustworthy kindness to an attempt to dominate.

Generally speaking, a handshake needs to be sensitive to the other person, communicating both an image of who you are and at the same time openness. The other person may have much smaller hands, or even arthritis. If so, the same firm handshake you offer to a big and burly rugby player will probably cause someone else discomfort, or even be painful.

You can observe how people shake hands and practise your own style in future meetings with people.

Different words

Consider some of the different ways in which people use words which can lead to an instant rapport or people getting side-tracked in communication. You can wonder why you ended up disagreeing, or talking about something you didn't mean to. These side-tracks are misunderstandings to do with people's diverse styles of communication.

The way people talk reflects how they think and vice versa. Often when people talk, they don't say exactly what they mean. This isn't because they are being deliberately underhand – it is just that there are conventions to talking, to do with politeness, social status and so on. Problems can come if someone else's convention is different from yours.

Generally in our choice of words there is both the obvious message and the hidden message.

For example, when you ask someone how they are, they will probably say 'I'm fine!', but is this how they really are? What is the hidden message and how do you know about it? They can use a different pitch, expression or body language to say anything from 'I'm very happy!' to 'I'm very upset!' as a hidden message behind the simple words 'I'm fine!'.

Judge for yourself

- Look at the contents of your wardrobe
- Look at yourself in the mirror from top to toe
- Look at other people – notice their image
- Dig out some old photos of yourself to see how you've changed

Use the table on the next page:

235

Rate the contribution your appearance is making towards achieving your goals by ticking the appropriate column:

ASPECTS OF IMAGE	Actively holding me back	Making it difficult	Neither one way nor another	Getting there	Doing a great job
Clothes: – tidiness					
– style					
– quality					
– age					
Shoes: – tidiness					
– style					
– quality					
– age					
Hair style					
Glasses style					
Contact lenses (or lack of)					
Briefcase					
Handshake					
Posture					
Cleanliness					
Facial Expression					
Weight					
Height					
Sparkle in the eyes					
Zest and energy					
Jewellery					
Attitude					
OVERALL IMPRESSION					

Now ask for some feedback from someone whose opinion you trust. Ask them how they would score you in this table. How far do they agree with your own self-assessment?

What does this tell you?

The difficulty comes if you are used to a different convention to someone else. These differences can be about:

- Culture, class, background, religion, gender or age
- Politeness – can be seen as reticence and 'caginess'
- Some people say 'no' and mean 'yes' – others definitely mean 'no'!
- Being straightforward and 'honest' seems to some like 'abruptness' or cruelty
- Humour: for some it is friendly, for others it is offensive
- Pauses in talking for some are for thought – for others they are vacant spaces to be filled
- Complaining: for some is a habit and for others it is an expression of a real grievance
- Asking questions for some is invasive interrogation, for others it is a genuine attempt to find out information
- What is loudness for some can be a normal volume for others
- Pitch and intonation – some people sound phoney when they are being sincere
- Names have power – some people use your name in a conversation to gain control and others just to be friendly
- For some people, technical words which are frequently used are jargon for others

Women's conversations with their women friends keep them in training for talking about their relationships with men, but many men come to such conversations with no training at all and an uncomfortable sense that this really isn't their event.

Deborah Tannen – *That's Not What I Meant!*

There are lots of other ways in which words can side-track communication. The thing to remember is that no one is in the wrong here if a side-track happens – it is just an unfortunate difference, which you can get around by becoming aware of it and trying out something else.

237

Can you think of a recent example where you were side-tracked in a conversation with someone?

   — *Describe what was going on here:*

   — *What could you have done differently?*

Tone of voice and body language

Words, voice and body language need to deliver the same message for you to be believed.

If you are talking on the phone, then the message is conveyed solely through your voice and your words. But if you are with someone your body language must convey the same information as your words. For example, if you say you are listening and at the same time you are looking out of the window or fiddling with your pencil, you probably won't be believed. It is vital that your body language, words and voice match each other.

Like words, there are many cultural and social differences in body language, so it is best to read all the signals of words, voice and appearance together. Otherwise, you may misinterpret someone folding their arms as being defensive or aggressive, when really they are just cold.

What you may or may not realise is that you are already an expert in body language. Observe people on a bus, a pub or another public space. Look at how people tend to naturally mirror each other's posture and gestures (very often they do so without noticing it themselves). Speculate on what you would read from their posture.

Notice when you are talking how much your words, your voice and your appearance match each other. Be prepared to adjust your style of communication to suit the person with whom you're talking. Don't just assume that everybody talks and thinks the way you do and if you don't get through it's because they are wrong.

Be prepared to match what you say and how you say it. That way, you'll stand more of a chance of the message getting through and being believed.

Body space   Another aspect of body language concerns the space we give ourselves and others.

How do you feel when you are travelling on a bus or train and people sit or stand very close to you? It is a fact of life that people invade our personal space in this situation, and this is why certain conventions are observed here, such as not making eye contact or even acknowledging the other person is there. Women perceive men as taking up more space on these occasions. In his book *Body Language*,[2] Allan Pease describes these spaces as zones. These zones are 'portable air bubbles' that we each have around us.

Zone distances   The size of these zones will vary depending upon the culture in which we have grown up. Crocodile Dundee was like most rural people who are used to bigger personal space zones than people in the city. Pease found that for people brought up in Australia, New Zealand, the UK and North America, the radius of the air bubble around people could be broken down into four distinct zones:

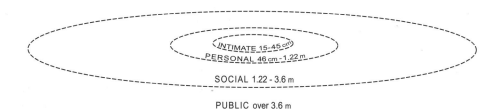

PUBLIC over 3.6 m

Intimate zone   Of all the zone distances this is by far the most important, as it is
15 – 45 cm   this zone that a person guards as if it were his own property. Only those who are emotionally close to that person are permitted to enter it. This includes lovers, parents, partner, children, close friends and relatives. There is also a sub-zone that extends up to 15 centimetres from the body which implies physical contact. This is the close intimate zone.

Personal zone   This is the distance that we stand from others at parties, social
46 cm – 1.22 m   functions and friendly gatherings.

Social zone   We stand at this distance from strangers, the plumber or carpenter
1.22 – 3.6 m   doing repairs, the postman, the shopkeeper, new employees at work and people whom we do not know very well.

Public zone   Whenever we address a large group of people, this is the
over 3.6 m   comfortable distance at which we choose to stand.

Being aware of the zones doesn't mean moving around with a tape measure around your waist, but simply to be more aware of the effect of distance.

You may feel that some people stand too close to you – or don't come close enough. You may have found yourself edging down the corridor because the person you are talking to keeps coming too close; or going up close to some people and seeing them back off.

If you wish people to react to you in a friendly, open way, then be sensitive to invading their space – it may be interpreted as aggressive and threatening.

Two clear invasions of body space are sexual harassment and bullying.

Sexual harassment

Many organisations have a sexual harassment policy and counsellors available to help people who believe they are being harassed. If it is happening to you, as a man, you may feel that you are unusual because you don't hear of any other men in similar circumstances. The reality is that, although women raise the majority of sexual harassment cases reported in many large organisations, men also make complaints. If people are coming too close to you, touching you or making unwelcome sexual suggestions or advances, find out if your employer has a harassment policy and decide what you want to do about it. Part of the solution may lie in assertiveness, which follows in this chapter.

It may be that she or he does not realise that their behaviour is harassing you. Similarly you may be behaving in a way that is harassing someone else.

In what ways, if any, do you experience harassment?

What do you want to do about it?

240

Which of your behaviours, if any, could someone else experience as harassment?

What are you going to do about it?

Bullying   Violence is also on a spectrum. On the one hand there is a friendly push or a joking punch and on the other hand there is threatening behaviour, bullying or physical harm.

If you are on the receiving end of behaviour that goes too far down the violence end of the spectrum you may experience the fear and the powerlessness that goes with it. There can be fear too of reprisals if you speak up, or in the workplace raise a grievance or complaint.

If on the other hand you are the person who doles out the threatening behaviour you may think that it is just a joke, a harmless bit of fun. Equally you may know that it has gone much further than that and you either don't know how to stop it or you don't want to stop it because you get some kick out of it.

Bullying can be verbal as well as physical. There can be a fine line between friendly mickey-taking and verbal abuse.

In what ways, if any, do you experience bullying?

What do you want to do about it?

Which of your behaviours, if any, could someone else experience as bullying?

What are you going to do about it?

If people feel good about themselves there is no reason for them to harass or bully anyone else. Underneath the harasser or bully there is a person who needs to deal with his/her own feelings. The chapter on feelings may help you more with this, as will the next page on assertiveness.

Assertiveness

The following definition of assertiveness applies throughout this workbook:

Assertiveness is a form of behaviour which demonstrates your self-respect and respect for others. Assertiveness is also concerned with dealing with your own feelings about yourself and other people, as much as with the end result.

- Assertiveness is about respecting others
- Assertiveness is about your own self-respect
- Assertiveness is about dealing with your feelings
- Assertiveness enables each of us to be more ourselves

When you are clear you are on-track with the way the message is being delivered between yourself and other people, assertiveness will enable you to be really clear about the message itself. It won't always mean that you reach full agreement with other people, but at least you will have been as clear as you can be about where you stand. This will count for a lot.

What assertiveness is and is not

People often confuse aggressive and assertive behaviour. So when they think of developing assertiveness skills they worry about being seen as aggressive. It is important to define what we mean. It's helpful to define aggressive and passive behaviour – as these are the ones that most of us seem to experience day-to-day – and then go on to clarify assertive behaviour.

Write down your own definitions of what aggressive, passive and assertive behaviour is here. Not the dictionary definitions – your own personal views.

Being aggressive is:

Being passive is:

Being assertive is:

Aggressive behaviour is:

- Getting your own way, no matter what
- Getting your own point across at other people's expense
- Getting people to do things they don't want to do
- Being loud and violent
- Interrupting others
- Winning at all costs
- Bullying

Recognise any of this? It's important to notice that we're talking about aggressive *behaviour* here, and not aggressive people, as we are all capable of behaving aggressively, passively and assertively.

Not all aggressive behaviour is obvious or direct. There is also indirect aggressive behaviour which can be:

- Conveyed in a polite way
- Quiet and apparently inoffensive
- Manipulating or tricking people
- Ignoring people
- Being silent
- Using sarcasm
- Putting people down, making them feel small
- Inoffensive on the surface

Most people have a tendency towards one form of behaviour rather than another, and vary their behaviour depending on the circumstances and their feelings at the time.

Aggressive behaviour doesn't come from being over-confident – quite the reverse; it comes from lack of confidence and fear. Underneath the blustering bully is a coward. It may be difficult to believe, but the person who's having a go at you is underneath feeling just as scared or threatened as a person behaving passively.

Passive behaviour is:
- Keeping quiet for fear of upsetting people
- Avoiding conflict
- Saying yes when you want to say no
- Always putting other people's needs first
- Not expressing your feelings
- Going along with things you don't like or agree with
- Apologising excessively
- Inwardly burning with anger and frustration
- Being vague about your ideas and what you want
- Justifying your actions to other people
- Appearing indecisive

Ever found yourself doing any of this? If so, you may have reached the point where you don't know what your views or feelings on a topic are, but somehow you have a vague feeling of dissatisfaction at being taken for granted, or not taken seriously.

Passive behaviour stems from lack of confidence. Turning passive behaviour into assertive behaviour will gradually build up your confidence.

Assertive behaviour is:
- Being open and honest with yourself and other people
- Listening to other people's point of view
- Showing understanding of other people's situations
- Expressing your ideas clearly, but not at the expense of others
- Being able to reach workable solutions to difficulties
- Making decisions – even if your decision is not to make a decision!
- Being clear about your point and not being sidetracked
- Dealing with conflict
- Having self-respect and respect for other people
- Being equal with others and retaining your uniqueness
- Expressing feelings honestly and with care

How often are you truly assertive by these standards? Most people find they can be assertive in some types of situations but tend to be aggressive or passive in others.

Why bother with assertiveness?

By behaving assertively:

- Your self-confidence increases
- You are properly understood
- Other people know exactly where they are with you
- You are more open to receiving feedback
- Your relationships are based on reality rather than illusion
- You stand a better chance of getting what you want
- You feel better for expressing your feelings
- You have fewer situations that are unresolved
- Even if you do not resolve a situation, you feel better for having tried

What is it that you want to change about your behaviour?

Assertiveness in practice

Does assertiveness always work? It depends on your objectives. It doesn't guarantee a particular outcome but if the process is followed it usually makes you feel that speaking up for yourself and expressing your feelings was worthwhile.

For example: Your boss asks you to stay late to finish a piece of work and you are perfectly assertive in your refusal to stay. Ultimately he or she still insists and unless you feel like resigning over it you realise that you will have to stay late. Your assertiveness hasn't affected the outcome – you still stay late.

However, behaving assertively in that situation has helped in a number of ways:

- You preserve your self-esteem: 'At least I said what I felt and explained properly without getting upset.'
- No one can ever say that you meekly agreed: 'You never said anything last time.'
- You may have provoked your boss into re-assessing you: 'I didn't realise he felt so strongly about that, he's got more to him than I thought.'

245

For the rest of this section and the next you will be looking at developing your assertive behaviour in a way that feels appropriate to you. It doesn't mean turning shy people into raving extroverts and it doesn't mean turning zany, fun people into boring grey clones.

Your assertiveness agenda

Write down the real situations you encounter, either at work or at home, where you would like to be more assertive.

Start off with one that is fairly easy. You could probably deal with it if you just got on with it.

FAIRLY EASY:

Go to the other extreme, and think of the most difficult or challenging situation that you encounter, or that you are avoiding. It may be something that makes you feel quite ill to think about, and you may think that nothing can be done about it. Write it down, all the same.

MOST DIFFICULT:

Transfer the easy situation from above to No. 1 and the difficult one to No. 10 on the next page. Now think of more examples. Make the low numbers the easier ones and the high numbers the more difficult ones.

Think of as many different instances as you can. Try to get a mixture of:
  – home/work
  – friends/relatives
  – big/little
  – short-term/long-term

Use the prompts on the next page if you need more ideas.

Next to each one write down how you deal with them now:
(passively, aggressively, indirectly aggressively).

SITUATIONS WHERE I WOULD LIKE TO BE MORE ASSERTIVE

1

2

3

4

5

6

7

8

9

10

Prompts   Here are some examples of the types of situations other people have chosen to work on. They are not in any order of difficulty because what may be easy for one person may be the most difficult for another, and the other way round. They are given purely as prompts to help you think of your own. Ignore them if you don't want to be prompted.

Personal
- Stopping noisy neighbours
- Dealing with a racist comment on the bus
- Dealing with banter that really gets to me
- Talking to demanding children
- Talking to my landlord about getting repairs done

Work
- Working hours interfering with personal life
- Saying no to requests for help when I'm overloaded
- Speaking up at meetings
- Standing up for what I believe in with more senior people
- Persuading my boss to let me do some of his/her work
- Dealing with a colleague who I know is lying to me
- Being bullied at work
- Being asked at an interview why I should get the job

247

Fight/flight syndrome

By definition, the 10 examples that you've just compiled are those when you do not behave assertively. Sometimes people are docile at work and bad-tempered at home, or doormats at home and downright bossy at work. Many people swing between aggressiveness and passiveness.

The fight/flight syndrome can explain your response to difficult events. Our bodies have evolved to help us deal with physical danger when we are faced with a difficult situation. They instinctively respond by putting us into a physically alert state (i.e. heart pounding, adrenaline flowing) which enables us to either fight the danger or run away.

Despite changes in society our instinctive response to difficult events is still either to fight (aggressive behaviour) or run away (passive behaviour).

While fighting or running away might have been good tactics in the Stone Age they aren't necessarily the most effective way to deal with situations in the 21st Century. However, it does explain why people don't seem to need courses on aggressive or passive behaviour – it just comes naturally.

It is also worth remembering that the root cause of aggressive and passive behaviour is fear or lack of self-confidence. Most of us are capable of swinging dramatically from one end of the scale to the other, for seemingly trivial reasons.

Building up notches

Ever had days when everything seems to go wrong? Some cope with this by keeping their heads down and keeping out of everyone's way, having days, months or even years like this, going home with resentment and frustration, until something snaps. Then they swing into an aggressive mode, lose their temper over something quite trivial, and everyone is astounded.

Every time you ignore a situation or choose not to deal with it and feel bad about it, it builds up a 'notch' of anger and resentment inside. Eventually, you get to the point where you blow up.

How do you feel immediately you blow up?

And how do you feel a bit later?

Most people feel great at the time and then guilty or ashamed not long afterwards. The danger is that if you feel so guilty later on that you feel bad about yourself, you may decide to keep quiet, and build up more notches; you then find yourself in a vicious circle of passive and aggressive behaviour.

You can allow yourself NOT to be assertive too. If you know you can choose to be assertive, you can equally choose NOT to assert yourself on any occasion. You may just not feel up to it that day, or you may decide it's not appropriate. You may still choose sometimes to be aggressive or passive because it seems the best short-term solution, but generally these behaviours won't build good long-term relationships.

How to be assertive

There are no set phrases, trick techniques, or magic words in assertiveness. There are five vital ingredients in any assertive process:

1
Listen

People who are successful at being assertive are good listeners. You may be able to listen well in some circumstances but listening gets more difficult the more complex or controversial the subject matter is. Assertiveness is often about ironing out tricky situations, so listening is a key skill.

2
Demonstrate the extent of your understanding

Have you experienced someone saying to you – 'I understand how you feel, however, …' and you are quite certain they don't understand. True assertiveness is not a set of trick phrases. In true assertiveness you need to demonstrate, by how you listen and by what you say, that you really have understood.

For example: 'You seem very angry and disappointed…' This gives the other person a chance to agree that you've got it right or correct it if you have it wrong.

For example : 'Disappointed – yes – but not really angry, more irritated because I've spoken about the same thing several times before.'

If you haven't understood then you need to say so.

249

3
Say what you
think and feel

Take responsibility for your feelings – check out Chapter 11 to pursue your feelings.

Be clear about what has given rise to your strong feelings and attribute them to the event or the behaviour – not the person. For example: 'I feel really disappointed that you haven't put petrol in the car when you said you would.'

4
Say specifically what
you want to happen

Dropping hints doesn't always work! Being clear about what you want to happen increases the possibility of getting what you want and minimises the chances of being misunderstood. Of course it doesn't guarantee that you get what you want; you have to be prepared for the other person to say no or have a different point of view. Listen to the response you get.

5
Joint solutions and
the consequences

Where there is a gap between what you want and what others want, you need to work out a joint solution. Note: Joint solution not compromise. Compromise means that neither of you get what you want. Joint solution means that both of you are satisfied. In exploring joint solutions consider the consequences of each choice on yourself and the others concerned. A joint solution may require more creativity.

How are you doing?

If you're still not sure whether you're behaving assertively or not, check your feelings about yourself and the other person. Remember that assertiveness is about feeling good about yourself and the other person. A useful shorthand way of looking at this is as follows:

Assertive	**Aggressive**
I'm OK	I'm OK
You're OK	You're not OK
Passive	**Depressive**
I'm not OK	I'm not OK
You're OK	You're not OK

Adapted from Thomas Harris's book
I'm OK, You're OK

Have a go!

Turn back to page 247 and your own real situations. Have a go at using assertiveness. Tackle your No 1. If there isn't an appropriate moment for it then pick any of your lower numbered situations – start small:

- Have a go at something which doesn't matter too much to you.
- Review your use of the five ingredients process
- Record below what happens:

Using assertiveness when you need to give feedback

As with saying 'no', many people avoid feedback as it can be uncomfortable. Giving feedback assertively gives opportunities for change to happen, and often clears the air. Feedback can be positive as well as negative, but even giving positive feedback can feel uncomfortable.

There are **5 steps in giving feedback assertively**:

1 Give specific examples of the behaviour
2 Say how you feel about the effect it has on you
3 Say what changes you'd prefer to see
4 Listen to the response (words, voice and body language)
5 Work out a joint solution, (not a compromise) to take you into the future – don't get bogged down in what has happened

Using assertiveness when you need to receive feedback

Remaining open to receive feedback takes courage. It is one of the ways you have to find out the effect you have on other people, and enables you to decide whether you want to change your behaviour or not. Do not fall into the trap of feeling you have to justify yourself.

There are **4 steps in receiving feedback assertively**:

1 Remain open – listen to what is being said and ask for specific examples to clarify your own understanding.
2 Let the other person know you've heard and understood the feedback, by giving the other person your immediate response
3 Take time to decide: Is it all true, is it partly true, is it totally false, what do you want to do?
4 Change your behaviour if you want to

Practise 'feedback situations'

If you are working through this workbook with other men, get together with two of them to practise giving and receiving feedback, and to do the exercise on the next page. If you are working through it on your own, see who among your family / friends / colleagues will be prepared to read the sections on assertiveness and join you in practising.

Practising has 4 steps:

1 Person One describes the scene and the characters briefly and in the practice tries to assert himself.
2 Person Two plays the other person, behaving as briefed by Person One.
3 If there is a third person, ask him/her to observe the practice and be ready to give feedback.
4 After the practice, participants and observers discuss what they have seen and heard and make constructive suggestions. You may then want to have another go!

Try practising giving and receiving feedback.

What did you learn?
Make notes here, and have a go at compliments.

Agenda for action

Write down situations in which you want to be more assertive.

For instance, inconsistency in someone's behaviour
  – When you aren't being listened to or being taken notice of
  – When you want to say 'no'

Tackle three of these over the next two weeks.

Being assertive with yourself

Difficulties with assertiveness often start before we open our mouths, as the most difficult relationship to handle is the relationship we have with ourselves. This sets the scene for our relationships with other people.

Being assertive with yourself:

- Stops you under-rating or over-rating yourself
- Identifies what you really need
- Makes you more productive
- Lets you know what you're good at
- Helps your actions follow your intentions

The conversations we have with ourselves have a huge effect on the outcomes of situations. They usually become self-fulfilling prophecies, so if you're feeling anxious and sceptical about something, it is likely that you will only 'tune in' to those aspects which fit with your anxiety and scepticism.

The final aspect of being assertive with yourself involves believing in your own feelings, and really valuing them. This may mean breaking away from your habitual patterns of behaviour, to really explain what's going on inside yourself, and stop making excuses to yourself.

Your assertive self:

- Is honest, rational, sane and realistic
- Is able to assess your own performance realistically and objectively
- Encourages you
- May get shouted down by the other voices

Think of situations in which you are now going to be more assertive with yourself:

Meaningful mission statement

Many companies and organisations now have mission statements, which are a way of defining and sometimes of changing the message they want people to receive about them.

If you were selling a product you would decide on the message that needs to be put across and then choose the right medium for doing this. Here you can look at the general message you put out, your 'mission statement' (or statements) which do justice to the product which you are selling, which is you.

Such mission statements should clearly express your key values and the core aspects of your identity and your goals in order to be really meaningful and not just a meaningless 'sound bite'. They can relate to your work, to your relationships, to the world and to your self-image.

A PERSONAL MISSION STATEMENT

Succeed at home first.
Seek and merit divine help.
Never compromise with honesty.
Remember the people involved.
Hear both sides before judging.
Obtain counsel of others.
Defend those who are absent.
Be sincere yet decisive.
Develop one new proficiency a year.
Plan tomorrow's work today.
Hustle while you wait.
Maintain a positive attitude.
Keep a sense of humour.
Be orderly in person and in work.
Do not fear mistakes – fear only the absence of creative, constructive,
     and corrective responses to those mistakes.
Facilitate the success of subordinates.
Listen twice as much as you speak.
Concentrate all abilities and efforts on the task at hand,
     not worrying about the next job promotion.

Rolfe Kerr[2]

What is your mission statement?

Where do you want to go now?

Think about:
- adding to the notes section, where you can record any useful ideas in the blank pages at the end of the workbook
- deciding which chapter to go to next

Anthony – Yorkshire

Past

Born in the Yorkshire Dales, my family consisted of my mother, father who died when I was seven years old, and an elder sister and brother. My mother raised the three of us and my memories of childhood are of a quiet, but not lonely, period of my life which has, to myself, continued throughout the intervening years.

Present

I'm 53 years old and still feel a novice in the world. I suppose I've realised that everyone is continually adding to experience and knowledge. I feel that I can interact with others' lives by adopting a calm and understanding attitude, unfortunately there are times when my forthright northern manner can lead to misunderstanding and resentment.

Future

Hopefully in the near future I shall be in a stable personal relationship and, having travelled during my working career, have come to realise that geographical preferences are not so very important as the relationship between people. People who knew my father referred to him as a kind and thoughtful man. I would like to be remembered this way.

Andy Durkin – Determined to prove others wrong about disabilities

Nothing could have prepared me for the negative attitude of potential employers towards people with disabilities. The feeling of being a failure was very strong. I also felt very isolated – how could anyone know what I felt inside? All of this could have clouded my future, as I began to believe that people only saw my disability – not my abilities or potential. Determination to prove myself was my driving energy. I felt I had to break the vicious circle that I had allowed to capture me.

An opening arrived in the form of being able to pass on my knowledge to other people who were on the Employment Training Scheme. I remember this temporary post with a great deal of pride. Life has a unique way of dealing with me and my rough edges. Despite at one time being a director of a company which ran a hotel, I was made redundant again and again, and it took a long time to bounce back from these experiences. Each time, I had been on a high wave and then I was cast on the shore, broken and rejected.

Dig deep was my only course of action. Use what I know, ring doorbells and show my face.

I also now spend time with my wife nurturing our relationship together. I have found her to be a true friend, someone who understands my inner feelings, someone to support me. Life will never be the same again if negative situations arrive, as now I have a rock and I am a rock in return.

The local authority ran a scheme to encourage disabled people into work. I passed the interview and was given a placement with the Personnel Section, which lasted for 14 months. Then I took my present post of Employment and Training Assistant. I have worked in that post for over two years, running 'breakthrough to work' programmes. My main role is to motivate and encourage disabled people who are experiencing some of what I had been through. I am able to lead by example and show what can be done with determination and a positive attitude.

I know that none of my experiences have been wasted. Each one has taught me valuable lessons, encouraging me to be the person I now am. When life throws its worst, I can survive and come back to challenge the limitations I and others put on me. I now know that if I believe in myself, others will believe in me too.

14

Your Story

" *When face to face with oneself, there is no cop-out* **"**

Duke Ellington

Your story   You have seen examples, stories and histories of other men
throughout the book. Now you can tell your own story, by way of a
graduation from this phase of your development.

This can be a powerful statement, a 'state of the union' of yourself
– an exercise in honesty as well as being brief and to the point. It
can serve to clarify and celebrate how you see yourself in this time
of your life.

The way you approach it is to:

Firstly, write two sentences which sum up your *past*.
Secondly, write two sentences which sum up your *present*.
Thirdly, write two sentences which sum up your *future*.

Some guidelines:
- Each statement, for past, present and future, must be just two sentences long. These sentences can include sub-clauses, lots of commas, dashes and so on, but the aim is to try and get to the heart of the matter by being as succinct as possible.
- For each sentence you can answer the questions provided, which is designed to prompt your thinking. You can choose to use these questions to frame your sentences or you can ignore them.
- Include the main themes of your whole life, as if you were painting a very broad picture, without too much detail – just the main colours and shapes of your life story.
- Allow yourself several attempts with each sentence, until you are happy with it.

Part one: PAST

Where did you come from?
What were the circumstances and atmosphere from your early years until now?

Part two: PRESENT

How do you see yourself now?
What are your best and worst characteristics?

Part three: FUTURE

Where will you be in a few (one, two, five or ten) years time?
How would you like to be remembered?

Having worked on these six sentences and got them to a state you are happy with, re-write them here as your story:

It can be a powerful experience to read this story aloud. It is something you can do with a loved one, close friend, or coaching partner.

Towards the future

Clay lies still, but blood's a rover:
Breath's a ware that will not keep
Up, lad: when the journey's over
There'll be time enough to sleep.

A. E. Housman – English poet

Where there is no vision, the people perish.   The Judaeo-Christian Bible

Here *Navigator* comes to an end, but your journey continues. Having vision, achieving whatever goals you have and moving forwards in your life can enable you to participate fully in a future which is both uncertain and full of opportunity.

This will not only have benefits for you but equally can achieve results for those around you, upon whom your life has an impact: in all spheres, from loved ones and friends, through work colleagues to passing acquaintances. Your life is part of a much bigger picture, and you contribute positively to it by knowing yourself and furthering your experience.

We hope that *Navigator* provides you with inspiration. It is only the map, however. You are the territory, with your efforts, dreams and capabilities – of which you have an abundance.

We wish you every success with your continuing journey.

All that we need is an acceptance that all men are born and remain, inherently powerful, sensitive, intelligent, outgoing and spontaneous, capable of unconditional love and able to act deliberately and to take responsibility for themselves.

Robert O'Neill Crossman, 1947-1996, *Singing Through the Summer*

I have seen the future, and it works.   Lincoln Steffens – American Journalist

Your Notes

Your Notes

Your Notes

Your Notes

Your Notes

Your Notes

Your Notes

Your Notes

Your Notes

Your Notes

Your Notes

Your Notes

Your Notes

Chapter notes

Chapter 2

1   Aaron Kipnis, *Knights Without Armor: a Guide to the Inner Lives of Men,* Indigo Phoenix Books, Santa Barbara, CA, 2004

2   Sources: UK Dept. of Education; University of Essex Economic & Social Research Council (ESRC); New Ways To Work Survey by New Ways to Work organisation; Central Office of Information (COI)

3   Steve Sonderman, *How to Build a Life-Changing Men's Ministry: Bringing the Fire Home to your Church,* Bethany House Publishers, Minneapolis, a division of Baker Publishing Group, 1996

Chapter 6

1   *Six Degrees of Separation,* Fred Schepisi (director), 1993

Chapter 7

1   Peter Baker and Mick Cooper, *The MANual: Complete Man's Guide to Life,* Thorsons London, 1996

2   Adrienne Burgess, *Fathers,* Carlton TV parenting campaign, 1997

3   Diana Mather, *Image Works for Men,* Thorsons London, 1996

4   Dr. Margaret Ryan, *Power and Influence in Organisations,* Manpower Services Commission, 1986

Chapter 8

1   ML Clements et. al, "The Erosion of Marital Satisfaction Over Time and How to Prevent it" from RJ Sternberg & M Hojjat M (eds.) *Satisfaction in Close Relationships,* Guildford Press, NY, 1997

2   James J. Forest, "Replication of Rated Relevance of Words in Self-Help Psychology Books"; *Psychological Reports* vol 83, 1998, page 674

3   John Gray, *Men are from Mars, Women are from Venus,* Thorsons London, 2002

4   J Dunn & C Kendrick, *Siblings: Love, Envy and Understanding,* Harvard University Press, 1982

5   BL Volling & J Belsky, 'The Contribution of Mother-Child and Father-Child Relationships to the Quality of Sibling Interaction', *Child Development,* 63 (5), 1992, pages 1209-1222

6   SS Feldmann, SC Nash & BG Aschenbrenner, 'Antecedents of Fathering', *Child Development,* 54, 1983, pages 1628-1634

7   *The Observer,* 4 January 1998

8   Steve Biddulph, *Raising Boys,* Harper Collins, London, 2003

9   "Belief in God", National Centre for Social Research, London, 1998

Chapter 10   1   From the Men's Health Forum website: **www.malehealth.co.uk**
2   *The Times,* 3 January 2004
3   *Observer Magazine,* 12 October 2003
4   N Bolger, A DeLongis, RC Kessler, E Wethington ,'The Contagion of Stress Across Multiple Roles', *Journal of Marriage and the Family* 51, 1989, pages 175-183
5   From the Men's Health Forum website, 2004: **www.malehealth.co.uk**

Chapter 11   1   C Rampage, 'Gendered Aspects of Marital Therapy' in NS Jacobson & AS Gurman (eds) *Clinical Handbook of Couple Therapy* (2nd edition), Guilford Press: New York, 1995, pages 261- 273
2   "Time to Nurture Those Soft Skills", *The Independent,* 29 May 1997

Chapter 12   1   Edward de Bono: *Handbook for the Positive Revolution,* Penguin Books, London 1992. Edward de Bono is regarded as one of the leading authorities in the world on the teaching of thinking. Web: **www.edwdebono.com**
2   Edward de Bono: *Six Thinking Hats,* Penguin Books, London 2000. Formal training in the method is available
3   Pearn Kandola Occupational Psychology, quoted in Men's Health, May 1997

Chapter 13   1   Prof Albert Mehrabian; *Silent Messages: Implicit Communication of Emotions and Attitudes,* Wadsworth, Belmont CA, 1981
2   Allan Pease, *Body Language: How to Read Others' Thoughts by Their Gestures,* Sheldon Press London 1997
3   Stephen R. Covey, *The 7 Habits of Highly Effective People,* Simon & Schuster, London 1992

Appendix 1

Useful Contacts

The authors　James Traeger, Jenny Daisley and Liz Willis

www.springboardconsultancy.com
www.jamestraeger.com

c/o Springboard, Holwell, East Down
Barnstaple, Devon EX31 4NZ
Tel: 01271 850828 Fax: 01271 850130
Email: office@springboardconsultancy.com
　　　james@jamestraeger.com

Useful organisations　**Alcoholics Anonymous**　　**www.alcoholics-anonymous.org.uk**
PO Box 1, Stonebow House, Stonebow, York YO1 7NJ
Administration: Tel: 01904 644026
24-hour helpline: Tel: 0845 769 7555
Email: aanewcomer@runbox.com
For people with concerns around or wishing to stop drinking alcohol

Cruse Bereavement Care　　　**www.cruse.org.uk**
Cruse House, 126 Sheen Road, Richmond, Surrey TW9 1UR
Administration: Tel: 020 8939 9530 Fax: 020 8940 7638
Day-by-day helpline: 0870 167 1677
Email: helpline@crusebereavementcare.org.uk
National network of support and information for bereavement

Cruse also runs a **Young Person's Helpline**:
Freephone: 0808 808 1677

Fathers Direct   **www.fathersdirect.com**
Herald House, Lamb's Passage, Bunhill Row, London, EC1Y 8TQ
Tel: 0845 634 1328 Email: mail@fathersdirect.com
For support around fatherhood

The Men's Health Forum   **www.menshealthforum.org.uk**
Tavistock House, Tavistock Square, London WC1H 9HR
Tel: 020 7388 4449 Email: peter.baker@menshealthforum.org.uk
*Provides an independent and authoritative voice for male health
and works to tackle the issues affecting the health and well-being
of boys and men in England and Wales.*

The Men's Health Forum also runs **www.malehealth.co.uk** – an
award-winning independent health information website for all men
and boys.

National Family Mediation   **www.nfm.u-net.com**
Alexander House, Telephone Avenue, Bristol BS1 4BS
Tel: 01392 271610 Fax: 01392 204227
Email:general@nfm.org.uk
*A network of over 60 local not-for-profit Family Mediation Services
in England and Wales offering help to couples, married or
unmarried who are in the process of separation and divorce.*

The Samaritans   **www.samaritans.org.uk**
Helpline: 08457 90 90 90 Email: jo@samaritans.org.uk
National free emotional support 24 hours a day.

Survivors UK   **www.survivorsuk.org**
2 Leathermarket Street, London SE1 3HN
Helpline: 0845 122 1201 E-mail: info@survivorsuk.org
Helpline for men who have experienced sexual violence

Working with Men   **www.workingwithmen.org**
320 Commercial Way, London SE15 1QN
Tel/Fax: 020 7732 9409 Email: info@workingwithmen.org
*A not-for-profit organisation that supports the development of work
with men through projects, resources, publications, training and
consultancy*

Websites

www.navigator-network.com
All about the network for Navigator trainers and supporters

www.direct.gov.uk/DisabledPeople
Disability rights, employment, education & training, financial support

www.stonewall.org.uk
Lesbian and gay issues

www.eoc.org.uk
The Equal Opportunities Commission

www.relate.org.uk
Marriage guidance/counselling

www.parentlineplus.org.uk
A UK registered charity, offering support to anyone parenting a child – the child's parents, step-parents, grandparents and foster parents

www.w-lb.org.uk
Work Life Balance Trust

www.angermanage.co.uk
British Association of Anger Management; also offers training & development

www.statistics.gov.uk
Government statistics

www.pcaw.org
Prostate Cancer Awareness

www.menstuff.org
A world resource on information for men

www.fathersdirect.com
National information service for fatherhood

www.young-voice.org
The views of children & young people

www.jrf.org.uk
Joseph Rowntree Foundation; source of important research on issues around men, masculinity & fatherhood

www.workingwithmen.org
Supports the development of men through projects, resources, publications, training and consultancy

www.sagepub.co.uk
Online journals including men & masculinities, gender & sexuality, family studies

www.fnf.org.uk
Families Need Fathers

www.homedad.org.uk
Support for stay at home fathers

www.menshealthforum.org.uk
Provides an independent and authoritative voice for male health and works to tackle the issues affecting the health and well-being of boys and men in England and Wales.

www.malehealth.co.uk
Run by the Men's Health Forum, this is an award-winning independent health information website for all men and boys.

www.edwdebono.com
Edward de Bono authorised website

www.emale.org.uk
Electronic newsletter for Christian men

www.paganmen.com
A place on the web for the spiritual male

www.workingfamilies.org.uk
Helps children, working parents and carers and their employers find a better balance between responsibilities at home and work

www.uk.gay.com
Gay support network

www.tcf.org.uk
The Compassionate Friends: support for bereaved parents and families after the death of a child

www.release.org.uk
Free, confidential advice to drug users, their families and friends

www.drc-gb.org
Disability Rights Commission; independent body aiming to stop discrimination and promote equality of opportunity for disabled people.

Appendix 2

Resources

BOOKS

Biographies/ Fiction

J G Ballard – *Empire of the Sun* – Flamingo – 1994

Philip Collins – *The Men from the Boys* – HarperCollins – 2003

Nick Hornby – *Fever Pitch* – Penguin Books – 2000

Nick Hornby – *High Fidelity* – Penguin Books – 2000

Tony Parsons – *Man and Boy* – HarperCollins – 2000

Jonathan Self – *Self Abuse* – Scribner – 2002

Disability Issues

Ian Greaves – *Disability Rights Handbook 2005/2006* – Disability Alliance Educational and Research Association – 2005

Families

Steve Biddulph – *Raising Boys* – HarperCollins – 2003

J Dunn & C Kendrick – *Siblings: Love, Envy and Understanding* – Harvard University Press – 1982

Robin Skynner & John Cleese – *Families and How to Survive Them* – Cedar Books – 1993

Health/Stress/Sexuality

Peter Baker and Mick Cooper – *The MANual: Complete Man's Guide to Life* – Thorsons London – 1996

Steve Carroll – *The "Which?" Guide to Men's Health* – Which? Books – 2003

David Servan-Schreiber – *Healing Without Freud or Prozac* – Rodale International – 2005

Charles Silverstein & Felice Picano – *The Joy of Gay Sex* (Third edition) – HarperCollins – 2004

John R Stowe – *Gay Spirit Warrior* – Findhorn Press – 1999

Men and Women   Steve Biddulph – *Manhood* – Vermilion – 2004

Robert Bly – *Iron John* – Rider & Co – 2001

Adrienne Burgess – *Fatherhood Reclaimed* – Vermilion – 1998

Alice H Eagly, Anne E Beall, Robert J Sternberg (eds) – *The Psychology of Gender* – Guilford Press – 2005

Susan Faludi – *Stiffed* – Vintage – 2000

Joyce K. Fletcher – *Disappearing Acts* – MIT Press – 2001

John Gray – *Men are from Mars, Women are from Venus* – Thorsons London – 2002

Shere Hite – *Sex and Business* – Financial Times Prentice Hall – 1999

Richard Lippa – *Gender, Nature and Nurture* – Lawrence Erlbaum – 2005

Allan and Barbara Pease – *Why Men Don't Listen and Women Can't Read Maps* – Orion – 2001

Deborah Tannen – *You Just Don't Understand* – Virago – 1992

Organisations, society   Richard Nelson Bolles – *What Color Is Your Parachute?* – Ten
and work   Speed Press – 2005

Alain de Botton – *Status Anxiety* – Penguin – 2005

David L Collinson, Jeff Hearn (eds) – *Men as Managers, Managers as Men* – Sage Publications – 1996

Dalmar Fisher, David Rooke, Bill Torbert – *Personal and Organisational Transformations* – Harthill – 2000

Daniel Goleman, Richard Boyatzis, Annie McKee – *The New Leaders* – Little Brown – 2002

Diana Mather – *Image Works for Men* – Thorsons London – 1996

Prof Albert Mehrabian – *Silent Messages: Implicit Communication of Emotions and Attitudes* – Wadsworth, Belmont CA – 1981

Michael Moore – *Stupid White Men* – Penguin – 2004

Allan Pease – *Body Language: How to Read Others' Thoughts by Their Gestures* – Sheldon Press – 1997

Tom Peters, Robert H. Waterman – *In Search of Excellence* – Profile Business – 2004

Brian Sykes – *Adam's Curse* – Corgi Adult – 2004

Neil Thompson – *Promoting Equality* – Palgrave Macmillan – 2003

Margaret J. Wheatley – *Leadership and the New Science* – Berrett-Koehler – 2001

Poetry   William Ayot – *Small Things that Matter* – Olivier Mythodrama – 2003

Abraham Gibson – *Violently Tender* – Pen Press – 2001

John Hegley – *The Sound of Paint Drying* – Methuen – 2003

Michael Leunig – *The Curly Pyjama Letters* – Viking Australia – 2001

Self Development   Ken Back, Kate Back – *Assertiveness at Work* – McGraw Hill – 2005

Edward De Bono – *Edward De Bono's Thinking Course* – BBC Books – 2004

Edward de Bono – *Handbook for the Positive Revolution* – Penguin Books – 1992.

Edward de Bono – *Six Thinking Hats* – Penguin Books – 2000

Tony Buzan – *How to Mind Map* – HarperCollins – 2002

Stephen R. Covey – *The 7 Habits of Highly Effective People* – Simon & Schuster – 1999

Howard Gardner – *Multiple Intelligences* – Basic Books – 1993

Kahlil Gibran – *The Prophet* – Arrow – 2000

Daniel Goleman – *Emotional Intelligence* – Bantam – 2005

Aaron Kipnis – *Knights Without Armor: a Guide to the Inner Lives of Men* – Indigo Phoenix Books, Santa Barbara, CA – 2004

Allan and Barbara Pease – *The Definitive Book of Body Language: The Secret Meaning Behind People's Gestures* – Orion – 2004

M. Scott Peck – *The Road Less Travelled* – Arrow – 1990

Robert M. Pirsig – *Zen and the Art of Motorcycle Maintenance* (25th Anniversary Edition) – Vintage – 1999

Elizabeth Kübler Ross – *On Death and Dying* – Simon & Schuster – 1997

Steve Sonderman – *How to Build a Life-Changing Men's Ministry* – Bethany House Publishers, Minneapolis, a division of Baker Publishing Group – 1996

FILMS

The following are films, which men on *Navigator* programmes have suggested as good at grappling with issues about men and masculinity

Billy Elliot – director: Stephen Daldry – 2000
Dead Poets Society – director: Peter Weir – 1989
Edward Scissorhands – director: Tim Burton – 1990
Full Metal Jacket – director: Stanley Kubrick – 1987
Good Will Hunting – director: Gus Van Sant – 1997
Goodbye Mr Chips – director: Sam Wood – 1939
Heat – director: Michael Mann – 1995
It's a Wonderful Life – director: Frank Capra – 1946
Lord of the Flies – director: Peter Brook – 1963
Pinocchio – director: Walt Disney – 1940
Ronin – director: John Frankenheimer – 1998
Shine – director: Scott Hicks – 1996
Six Degrees of Separation – director: Fred Schepisi – 1993
Stand by Me – director: Rob Reiner – 1986

Taps – director: Harold Becker – 1981
The Full Monty – director: Peter Cattaneo – 1997
The Shawshank Redemption – director: Frank Darabont – 1994
Three Men and a Baby – director: Leonard Nimoy – 1987
Tootsie – director: Sydney Pollack – 1982
What Women Want – director: Nancy Meyers – 2000

Inspirational songs

These songs have been recommended by men involved in *Navigator* – as concerned with masculinities, men's joys and desires and pain. Many are therefore significant for men and men's development. Men have written millions of songs – many focus on love or related themes – but these are too many to mention. These songs and lyrics show that it is just a myth to say men don't feel or express emotions!

MEN'S GREATEST HITS:

A Better Man – Robbie Williams
A Man's World – James Brown
As You Are – Travis
Boys Don't Cry – The Cure
Consideration – Reef
Daniel – Elton John
Duet from *The Pearl Fishers* – Georges Bizet
Father and Son – Ronan Keating, featuring Yusuf
He Ain't Heavy, He's My Brother – The Hollies
High and Dry – Radiohead
I Am What I Am – Gloria Gaynor
I Shot the Sheriff – Bob Marley
It Ain't Me Babe – Bob Dylan
It Ain't What You Do It's The Way That You Do It – Little Richard
Jealous Guy – John Lennon
Money for Nothing – Dire Straits
Mother – John Lennon
My Father's Eyes – Eric Clapton
No Woman No Cry – Bob Marley
Over and Over – Kings X
Porcelain – Moby
Remember Me (from *Dido and Aeneas*) – Henry Purcell
Saturday Night is Alright for Fighting – Elton John
Slip Sliding Away – Paul Simon
Stand by Me – John Lennon
Stand by my Woman – Lenny Kravitz
Starman – David Bowie
Supreme – Robbie Williams

The Boxer – Simon and Garfunkel
The Drugs don't Work – The Verve
The Living Years – Mike and the Mechanics
The Man who Told Everything – Doves
The Only Living Boy in New York – Simon and Garfunkel
Your Mother and I – Loudon Wainwright III

Please talk to me: e-mail me with your additions or ideas......
Chris Sharpe – 29 St Marys Rd. Ipswich IP4 4SW Suffolk
01473 278123 chris@sharpe99.freeserve.co.uk

Inspirational poems

Over the years many poems have been read, talked about and enjoyed during *Navigator* programmes. We decided to select a few that have been mentioned by many, in order to inspire you on your own development journey.

If

*If you can keep your head when all about you
Are losing theirs and blaming it on you.
If you can trust yourself when all men doubt you
But make allowance for their doubting too;
If you can wait and not be tired by waiting,
Or being lied about, don't deal in lies,
Or being hated, don't give way to hating,
And yet don't look too good, nor talk too wise:*

*If you can dream – and not make dreams your master,
If you can think – and not make thoughts your aim;
If you can meet with Triumph and Disaster
And treat those two impostors just the same;
If you can bear to hear the truth you've spoken
Twisted by knaves to make a trap for fools,
Or watch the things you gave your life to, broken,
And stoop and build 'em up with worn out tools:*

*If you can make one heap of all your winnings
And risk it on one turn of pitch-and-toss,
And lose, and start again at your beginnings
And never breathe a word about your loss;
If you can force your heart and nerve and sinew
To serve your turn long after they are gone,
And so hold on when there is nothing in you
Except the Will which says to them: 'Hold on!'*

*If you can talk with crowds and keep your virtue,
Or walk with Kings – nor lose the common touch,
If neither foes nor loving friends can hurt you,
If all men count with you, but none too much;
If you can fill the unforgiving minute
With sixty seconds' worth of distance run,
Yours is the Earth and everything that's in it,
And – which is more – you'll be a Man, my son!*

Rudyard Kipling

from *Letters to a Young Poet*

I want to beg you as much as I can to be patient
Toward all that's unsolved in your heart,
And to learn to love the questions themselves,
Like locked rooms.
Or like books that are written in a foreign tongue.

Do not seek the answers that cannot be given to you,
Because you would not be able to live them,
And the point is to live everything.

Live the questions now.
Perhaps you will then, gradually,
Without noticing it,
Live along some distant day
Into the answer.

Rainer Maria Rilke,
translated by M D Herter Norton

He was a Man

In Menswear
He shot a brightly coloured sportscoat
With his trusty bow.

He harpooned
A large, fat couch
In the furniture department.

He clubbed
A pop-up toaster
In the electrical section

With his bare hands
He fought a king-size quilt
In Bedding.

He cast his net in Footwear
And caught
A magnificent pair of slippers.

He was a hunter.
He was a provider.
He was a MAN.

Michael Leunig, from *Poems 1972-2002*

Desiderata

Go placidly amid the noise and haste and remember what peace there may be in silence. As far as possible without surrender be on good terms with all persons.

Speak your truth quietly and clearly; and listen to others, even the dull and ignorant; they too have their story.

Avoid loud and aggressive persons; they are vexatious to the spirit.

If you compare yourself with others, you may become vain and bitter; for always there will be greater and lesser persons than yourself. Enjoy your achievements as well as your plans. Keep interested in your own career, however humble; it is a real possession in the changing fortunes of time. Exercise caution in your business affairs; for the world is full of trickery. But let this not blind you to what virtue there is; many persons strive for high ideals; and everywhere life is full of heroism.

Be yourself. Especially do not feign affection. Neither be cynical about love; for in the face of all aridity and disenchantment it is as perennial as the grass.

Take kindly the counsel of the years, gracefully surrendering the things of youth. Nurture strength of spirit to shield you in sudden misfortune. But do not distress yourself with imaginings. Many fears are born of fatigue and loneliness. Beyond a wholesome discipline, be gentle with yourself.

You are a child of the universe; no less than the trees and the stars, you have a right to be here.

And whether or not it's clear to you, no doubt the universe is unfolding as it should. Therefore be at peace with God, whatever you conceive God to be; and whatever your labours and aspirations, in the noisy confusion of life keep peace with your soul.

With all its sham, drudgery and broken dreams, it's still a beautiful world. Be cheerful. Strive to be happy.

Max Ehrmann

from *Campos de Castilla*

Everything comes and everything passes
But our lot is to pass
Pass making paths
Paths on the sea

Never pursue glory
Nor keep in the memory
Not even this song of mine

I love useful worlds
Weightless ones and gentle ones
Like floating bubbles

I would like to see these bubbles paint a picture
from sun and flying red dye
Under a shaking blue sky
And then suddenly they vanish and are gone

Traveller there is no path
Only stars in the sea

A long time ago here in this place
Where the woods are covered today with Gorse
The poet's voice was heard shouting:

'Traveller there is no path
You make a path as you walk
Blow by blow
Verse by verse'

The poet died far from home
He was covered with the dust of a Country over the border
But from far away his voice was still heard booming:

'Traveller there is no path
You make a path as you walk
Blow by blow
Verse by verse'

When the little goldfinch sings no more
When the poet becomes a pilgrim
When praying is worth nothing:

'Traveller there is no path
You make a path as you walk
Blow by blow
Verse by verse'

Antonio Machado,
(last two lines added by J M Serrat)
translated by Hugh Dennis

Nos Galan

Oer yw'r gwr sy'n methu caru
Hen fynyddoedd annwyl cymru
Iddo ef a'u car gynesaf
Gwyliau llawen flwyddyn nesaf

I'r helbulus oer yw'r biliau
Sydd yn dyfod yn y Gwyliau
Gwranda bregeth mewnun pennill
Byth na waria fwy na'th ennill

Oer yw'r eira ar Eryri
Er fod gwrthban gwlanen arni
Oer yw'r bobol na ofalan'
Gwrdd a'u gilydd, ar Nos Galan

John Ceiriog Hughes, from *Gweithiau Ceiriog*

I Will Not Die an Unlived Life

I will not die an unlived life
I will not live in fear of falling
Or of catching fire
I choose to inhabit my days
To allow my living to open me
Making me less afraid
More accessible
To loosen my heart
So that it becomes a wing, a torch, a promise
I choose to risk my significance.
To live so that that which comes to me as seed
Goes to the next as blossom
And that which comes to me as blossom
Goes on as fruit.

Dawna Markova

291

from *Selected poems from*
the Divani Shamsi Tabriz

What is to be done, O Moslems? for I do not recognize myself.
I am neither Christian, nor Jew, nor Gabr, nor Moslem.
I am not of the East, nor of the West, nor of the land, nor of the sea;
I am not of Nature's mint, nor of the circling heaven.
I am not of earth, nor of water, nor of air, nor of fire;
I am not of the empyrean, nor of the dust, nor of existence, nor of
     entity.
I am not of India, nor of China, nor of Bulgaria, nor of Saqsin
I am not of the kingdom of Iraqian, nor of the country of Khorasan
I am not of the this world, nor of the next, nor of Paradise, nor of Hell
I am not of Adam, nor of Eve, nor of Eden and Rizwan.
My place is the Placeless, my trace is the Traceless;
'Tis neither body nor soul, for I belong to the soul of the Beloved.
I have put duality away, I have seen that the two worlds are one;
One I seek, One I know, One I see, One I call.
He is the first, He is the last, He is the outward, He is the inward;
I know none other except 'Ya Hu' and 'Ya man Hu.'
I am intoxicated with Love's cup, the two worlds have passed out
     of my ken;
I have no business save carouse and revelry.
If once in my life I spent a moment without thee,
From that time and from that hour I repent of my life.
If once in this world I win a moment with thee,
I will trample on both worlds, I will dance in triumph for ever.
O Shamsi Tabriz, I am so drunken in this world,
That except of drunkenness and revelry I have no tale to tell.

Rumi,
edited and translated by Reynold A Nicholson

from *Bhagavad Gita*

When you are inspired by some great purpose, some extraordinary
project, all your thoughts break their bonds; your mind transcends
limitations, your consciousness expands in every direction, and
you find yourself in a new, great and wonderful world. Dormant
forces, faculties and talents become alive, and you discover
yourself to be a greater person by far than you ever dreamed
yourself to be.

Patajali, 1st – 3rd century BCE,

Tao te Ching – Chapter 44

Fame or integrity: which is more important?
Money or happiness: which is more valuable?
Success or failure: which is more destructive?

If you look to others for fulfilment,
you will never truly be fulfilled.
If your happiness depends on money,
you will never be happy with yourself.

Be content with what you have;
rejoice in the way things are.
When you realize there is nothing lacking,
the whole world belongs to you.

Lao Tzu

Human Family

I note the obvious differences in the human family,
Some of us are serious, some thrive on comedy.
Some declare their lives are lived as true profundity,
and others claim they really live the real reality.

The variety of our skin tones can confuse, bemuse, delight,
brown and pink and beige and purple, tan and blue and white.
I've sailed upon the seven seas and stopped in every land,
I've seen the wonders of the world, not yet one common man.

I know ten thousand women called Jane and Mary Jane,
but I've not seen any two who really are the same.
Mirror twins are different although their features jibe,
and lovers think quite different thoughts while lying side by side.

We love and lose in China, we weep on England's moors.
We laugh and moan in Guinea, and thrive on Spanish shores.
We seek success in Finland, are born and die in Maine.
In minor ways we differ, in major we're the same.

I note the obvious differences between each sort and type, but
we are more alike, my friends, than we are unalike.
We are more alike, my friends, than we are unalike.
We are more alike, my friends, than we are unalike.

Maya Angelou

Other books from Hawthorn Press

'"Inspir-actical" is how I would describe Springboard. It inspires women to decide what they most want to achieve and then, very practically, helps them do it. It's fun and involving.'

Valerie Hammond,
Chief Executive Officer, Roffey Park Management Institute

Springboard
Women's Development Workbook
Liz Willis and Jenny Daisley

Illustrated by Viv Quillin

Springboard helps you do what you want to do in your life and work. It gives you the ideas and skills to take more control of your life and then gives you the boost in self confidence to start making things happen. *Springboard* is for all women at work; whether you are in full time or part time employment, considering employment, wanting to return to work, just starting out, or approaching retirement – *Springboard* helps you to be the best you can be!

Springboard is a workbook packed with ideas, exercises and examples that you can either work through on your own, or with two or three others. It is down-to-earth, practical and full of positive thinking and good humour, with the points illustrated with cartoons and real case studies. This new edition is fully revised and updated. You can work through the workbook on its own or as part of the Springboard Women's Development Programme.

Contents include; assertiveness; setting goals; what you've got going for you; finding support; the world about you; blowing your own trumpet; more energy – less anxiety; making things happen; your personal resource bank; balancing home and work; networking; useful addresses.

Personal Development series; 5th edition; 320pp; 297 x 210mm; illustrations; cartoons; paperback; 1 869 890 10 8

If you could have anything, what would it be?

Are you making the most of your potential?

Have you ever felt there was something you are supposed to achieve, but can't seem to start?

Don't just dream about it – make it happen!

'We're not Sleeping Beauties, we're women, capable of being and doing anything and everything we want to ... So go for it – say 'Yes' ... Change your life, our community, the world.'
Glenda Jackson, MP

'At last! A book for realising your dreams – a reference for life.'
Maureen Davis

Springing Forward
Gina Harris and Liza Edwards

Welcome to the essential handbook for *all* women wanting to make the most of who they are. *Springing Forward* is packed full of practical steps, sound advice and inspiration to support you – whatever your goal, whatever your situation. Each stage is also supported by quotes and stories from women around the world, drawing on the global success of the Springboard Women's Development Programme, and celebrating women's achievements.

Springing Forward shows how women can make genuine, positive changes to their everyday lives. Most importantly, the writers realise that you do have priorities other than nurturing yourself, and they tackle the path ahead with practical, realistic advice, frankness and a good dose of humour.

Springing Forward began as a project to celebrate the international success of The Springboard Women's Development Programme, which was developed by Liz Willis and Jenny Daisley in 1989. In doing the research for the project, Gina Harris and Liza Edwards realised that so many of the women had inspirational stories that it grew into a book to inspire and support other women to achieve their own goals.

Both writers demonstrate wide knowledge and experience of development issues, particularly the dilemma faced by women wanting to achieve something 'for themselves' when other priorities demand attention.

Topics covered include:

- Bringing the ideal into the real
- Healthy selfishness
- Getting organised – space, finances and time
- The internet and how real people can benefit
- Values, priorities and acting on decisions
- Genuine communication
- Simplicity, serenity and the future
- ... and enjoying it all!

Personal Development series; 128pp; 210 x 148mm; paperback; 1 869 890 40 X

Confronting Conflict
A first-aid kit for handling conflict
Friedrich Glasl

Conflict costs! When tensions and differences are ignored they grow into conflicts, injuring relationships, groups and organisations. So, how can we tackle conflict successfully?

Confronting Conflict is authoritative and up to date, containing new examples, exercises theory and techniques. You can start by assessing the symptoms and causes of conflict, and ask, 'Am I fanning the flames?' And then consider, 'How can I behave constructively rather than attack or avoid others?' *Confronting Conflict* will be useful for managers, facilitators, management lecturers and professionals such as teachers and community workers, mediators and workers in dispute resolution.

Conflict and Peace Building series; 192pp; 216 x 138mm; paperback; 1 869 890 71 X

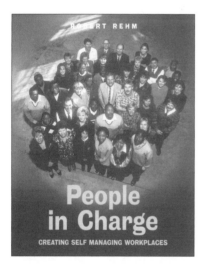

'Frankly, I find most books on this subject useless. This one is different. It is filled with practical theories, and business related examples, that I can use on a daily basis.'
Kevin Purcell, Director of Organization Consulting, Microsoft Corporation

People in Charge
Creating self managing workplaces
Robert Rehm

A step-by-step guide to designing self managing workplaces. Powerful and practical, Participative Design enables companies to create more productive workplaces and better results. Here are the tools for creating self managing workplaces using Participative Design. The concepts, do-it-yourself guide and helpful examples show how people can re-design their work. The result is a more productive workplace full of energy, learning, quality and pride. And people in charge of their work.

Participative Design was devised by Fred Emery in the 1970's. Here, Robert Rehm shows how managers and workers can use Participative Design to do a better job. Examples include the US Federal Courts, a Prudential call centre, the South African Land Bank, retail stores, a wine company and the conductor-less Orpheus Orchestra of New York.

Social Ecology series; 288pp; 243 x 189mm; paperback; 1 869 890 87 6

Parenting Matters
Ways to bring up your children using heart and head
Parentline Plus

Parenting Matters helps you bring up loving and happy children. Here is the heart to becoming the more confident, sensitive relaxed, firm and caring parent that you truly are – enjoying your children and family.

Parenting Matters is a workbook packed with ideas, exercises and examples for personal use. It supports your learning on the course run by Parentline Plus. This sensible and positive approach has been successfully developed by parents for parents over many years. Contents include: understanding children's needs and behaviour; positive communication; assertiveness; listening; dealing with feelings; building self-esteem; love and discipline; looking after parents' needs; setting up support groups.

Parenting and Health series; 240pp; 297 x 210mm; paperback; 1 869 890 16 7

Parents' Comments:
*'It is changing my life – wish I could have done this years ago.
'This course has really helped improve our family life.'
'I have learnt some very good ideas to help me get on better with my children.'*

Being a Parent
Parentline Plus

Being a parent is one of the most important jobs in the world, because parents hold the future in their hands. Parents need all the help they can get. Yet many battle on without any support or guidance.

There are many different approaches to parenting. In our multi-cultural world, there is no one way of bringing up children that is right for everyone. *Being a Parent* helps you find out what works best for you and your children. This friendly and helpful book can be used on its own or as a workbook for the Parentline Plus course, Understanding Children 1, which is accredited by the National Open College Network.

Parenting and Health series; 96pp; 297 x 210mm; paperback; 1 869 890 81 7

'This book makes a notable contribution because it tries to tackle the issues in a positive way, without reducing opportunities for girls. It emphasises positive steps that teachers can take.'
Ted Wragg, Professor of Education at Exeter University

Bringing the Best out in Boys
Communication Strategies for Teachers
Lucinda Neall

Boys aren't bad, they're just different, says Lucinda Neall. Her time tested communication strategies help get the best out of boys. The techniques for tackling difficult behaviour will result in better classroom co-operation and learning – so that everyone benefits. Parents and home educators will find her insights into boys' psychology useful too!

'Strongly recommended.'   Times Education Supplement

'A godsend to harassed classroom teachers.'
Mike Shankland, Liverpool Hope University

Education series; 288pp; 210 x 148mm; paperback; 1 903458 29 3

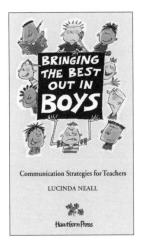

PAL (UK) format video

Bringing The Best Out In Boys (video)
Communication strategies for teachers

Using real-life classroom scenes and lively interviews, this video and facilitator's guide explores what boys think about school, what motivates and de-motivates them, and suggests communication strategies to engage them in learning. Topics featured include: channelling boys' energy; structure, boundaries and discipline; praise and admiration; and teaching styles. The video can be used by individual teachers, small groups or as the basis for an in-service training session for larger groups. The facilitator's guide gives a summary of the video, highlighting the key points and commenting on the examples of classroom practice.

Education series; video with 48pp facilitator's guide; 198 x 114mm; 1 903458 41 2

The Good Sleep Guide
**The step-by-step guide to good sleep
for babies from birth-18 months**
Angela Henderson

It's the middle of the night, you've got to go to work in the morning – and your baby won't go to sleep. This book is for you.

Recommended by thousands of health visitors, this step-by-step guide offers tried and tested techniques to prevent the misery of months of sleepless nights and cure sleep problems in babies 6 months and older.

**Parenting and Health series; 112pp; 210 x 148mm;
paperback; 1 903458 35 8**

'A voice of sanity in the fog of new parenthood.'
Joanna Briscoe,
The Independent

Sound Sleep
Calming and helping your baby or child to sleep
Sarah Woodhouse

'Whether you have a colicky three-month old or fretful toddler, the advice and routines outlined within this book provide both practical and realistic solutions to help you reach the holy grail of parenting – a soundly sleeping baby! There's a great section on how to decipher your baby's cries, so that you know what you're dealing with, and useful checklists that free up frazzled brain power in stressful moments. A refreshing approach that recognises every baby – and every parent – is different.'
Baby and You

**Parenting and Health series; 144pp; 246 x 189mm;
paperback; 1 903458 27 7**

Muddles, Puddles and Sunshine
Your activity book to help when someone has died
Winston's Wish

Muddles, Puddles and Sunshine offers practical and sensitive support for bereaved children. Beautifully illustrated, it gives a helpful series of activities and exercises accompanied by the friendly characters of Bee and Bear.

'Used with a supportive adult this is a useful resource, which when completed will be a wonderful memento that will help the grieving process.'
Journal of the National Association of Hospital Play Staff

Early Years series; 32pp; 297 x 210mm landscape; full colour illustrations; paperback; 1 869 890 58 2

The Parent and Child Group Handbook
A Steiner/Waldorf approach
Dot Male

This inspiring resource guide draws on Dot Male's wealth of experience in working with parents and young children. Illustrated with lively case studies, her book offers a comprehensive guide to setting up and running a parent and child group based on Rudolf Steiner's unique, holistic approach to child development. The contents include: structuring a session; appropriate toys and activities; the shared meal; circle time; festivals; health, safety and legal issues; marketing, publicity and fundraising.

This unique and much needed book gives a convincing argument for the value of these groups, for both parent and child. Both inspiring and immensely practical, it offers the group leader the insight and means to create a truly meaningful and appropriate experience within a parent and child group setting.'
Lynne Oldfield, Director,
London Waldorf Early Childhood Training Course

Early Years series; 256pp; 246 x 189mm; paperback; 1 903458 46 3

Above: typical double-page spread

Below: detail, actual size

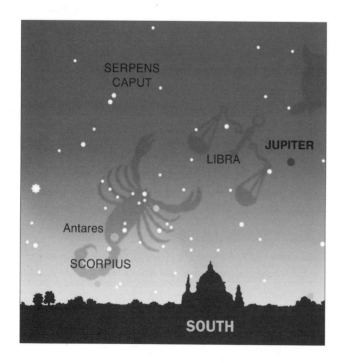

Stargazers' Almanac
Monthly guide to the stars and planets

Explore the wonders of the night skies with the *Stargazers' Almanac* – no telescope required! Track the planets, locate the Milky Way, discover the heavenly Giraffe, Orion's dogs and Draco the dragon, recognise the signs of the zodiac and watch meteor showers and other planetary phenomena. The beautiful, easy to use colour charts make this a great introduction to astronomy, perfect for beginners, children and back-yard stargazers.

Each monthly chart features two views of the night sky looking north and south; a visual guide to the phases of the moon; and key planets and other objects. The observing notes include fascinating insights into the science, history, folklore and myths of the stars and planets.

Stargazers' Almanac also includes:
- Advice on how to navigate the night sky
- Overhead map of the sky
- Reference plan of constellations
- Guide to the signs of the zodiac and how they relate to the stars
- Glossary of constellations and Latin names; glossary of brightness of stars
- Information on the British Astronomical Association's Campaign for Dark Skies

'An ideal introduction to the night sky.'
    Dr D. Storey, Worthing Astronomical Society

Art and Science series; 32pp; 420 x 297mm landscape; paperback

PUBLISHED ANNUALLY
Printed on environmentally friendly paper and packaged in an attractive gift box, *Stargazers' Almanac* is an ideal Christmas gift which will last the whole year!

Ken Sprague – People's Artist
John Green

This lively portrait of the life, art and politics of Ken Sprague shows how art can transform lives, deepen social engagement and build bridges. Here is a selection of Ken's work, including his Guernica cartoon as a boy, poster for Martin Luther King and war pictures from Iraq and Kosovo.

'The true heir of William Morris – achieved what William Morris could only dream of.'

Martin Rowson, cartoonist

Art and Science series; 160pp; 275 x 215mm; includes colour section; paperback; 1 903458 34 X

Orders   If you have difficulties ordering Hawthorn Press books from a bookshop, you can order direct from:

Booksource
32 Finlas Street, Glasgow, G22 5DU
Tel: (08702) 402182
Fax: (0141) 557 0189
E-mail: orders@booksource.net

Further information/
Book catalogue   Hawthorn Press
1 Lansdown Lane, Stroud
Gloucestershire, GL5 1BJ, UK
Tel: +(44) (0) 1453 757040
Fax: +(44) (0) 1453 751138
E-mail: info@hawthornpress.com
Website: **www.hawthornpress.com**

Dear Reader

If you wish to follow up your reading of this book, please tick the boxes below as appropriate, fill in your name and address and return to Hawthorn Press:

☐ Please send me a catalogue of other Hawthorn Press books.

☐ Please send me details of Personal Development events and courses.

My feedback about Personal Development:

Name _____

Address _____

_____

_____

Postcode _____ Tel no _____

Please return to:
Hawthorn Press, Hawthorn House, 1 Lansdown Lane,
Stroud, Glos. GL5 1BJ, UK

or Fax (01453) 751135

NAV 2006